Ten Steps *to* Helping *your* Child Succeed *in* School

WORKBOOK

THIS WORKBOOK BELONGS TO:

_____

Ten Steps *to* Helping *your* Child Succeed *in* School

WORKBOOK

MYCHAL WYNN

CONTRIBUTING EDITORS

ERYN DAVILA • SERITA DODSON

RISING SUN PUBLISHING

Publisher's Cataloging-In-Publication Data

Wynn, Mychal.

Ten steps to helping your child succeed in school. Workbook / Mychal Wynn ; contributing editors, Eryn Davila, Serita Dodson. -- 1st ed.

p. : ill. ; cm.

Includes bibliographical references and index.
ISBN-13: 978-1-880463-79-6
ISBN-10: 1-88046-379-2

1. Education--Parent participation--Problems, exercises, etc. 2. Learning, Psychology of--Problems, exercises, etc. 3. Academic achievement--Problems, exercises, etc. I. Davila, Eryn. II. Dodson, Serita. III. Title.

LB1048.5 .W961 2008
371.192/076

2008937364

Library of Congress Control Number: 2008937364
ISBN-13: 978-1-880463-79-6
ISBN-10: 1-880463-79-2

The poems, *A Curious Child, A Pledge to Myself, Dream-Builder's Affirmation,* and *Children We Care,* reprinted by permission of the author, Mychal Wynn. Illustrations by Mychal-David Wynn.

P.O. Box 70906
Marietta, GA 30007-0906
770.518.0369/800.524.2813
FAX 770.587.0862
E-mail: info@rspublishing.com
Web site: http://www.rspublishing.com

Printed in the United States of America.

Acknowledgments

I would like to acknowledge my wife, Nina, who, as a wife, mother, confidant, and business partner has greatly contributed to the ideas contained within this book. She has put into practice the strategies as she has successfully guided our older son's oftentimes complex and frequently frustrating journey from preschool through high school, into his acceptance via Early Decision into Amherst College, and, our younger son's journey via a different set of issues and obstacles, successfully from preschool into high school. She has also inspired, enlightened, and encouraged other children and their families along their parallel journeys from preschool into college.

I would also like to thank my niece, Tishandra de Courcy, a mother of three, for her efforts in ensuring that this workbook is usable and doable for any parent.

I would like to acknowledge elementary school teachers and contributing editors, Eryn Davila and Serita Dodson, who shared of their time and made an invaluable contribution to the activities contained in this book. Their contribution ensures that teachers, counselors, administrators, mentors, and coaches, who often serve as surrogate parents, can utilize the activities to enhance their relationships and provide the necessary guidance that students need to achieve success in school and prepare themselves for postsecondary education and career opportunities. I would also like to thank my good friend, Dr. Glenn Bascome, who, despite his many responsibilities as a husband, parent, and middle school teacher, makes himself available to provide editorial assistance.

Lastly, I would like to thank my mother and father who, with limited education and little by way of parent resources, guided my way out of poverty, into college, and into a life of options and opportunities, previously unimaginable.

Dedication

This book is dedicated to my sons, Mychal-David and Jalani, the thousands of students and parents I meet each year, and to those who sacrifice each day on behalf of students and their dreams.

Table of Contents

Introduction

Mychal and his wife, Nina, have firsthand experience with the many challenges and frustrations facing parents.

"Jalani hit a little girl and bit a little boy."
"Jalani would not go to sleep at nap time."
"Mychal-David would not stop talking in class."
"Jalani used bad words today."
"Mychal-David has not been turning in his work."
"Jalani would not be quiet at story time."
"Mychal-David broke the pencil sharper."
"Jalani kicked a hole in the wall."
"Jalani would not sit in time-out, so he was sent to the office and you have to come and get him right now!"

If responding to the frequent notes, meeting with teachers, counselors, and the principal, and dealing with their sons' behaviors were not enough, Mychal and Nina had to develop, revise, develop, and revise again strategies to get their older son to do his class work ("I am not motivated in class"), turn in his homework, and bring home the many notices that he received from school.

"When our older son, Mychal-David, graduated from the fifth grade, Nina and I celebrated. This day marked the end of another school year. For eight years, dating back to his preschool days at the First Lutheran Church in Carson, California, we prayed for solutions, researched everything that we could find about parenting and teaching, developed and implemented strategies, and prayed again for the wisdom and strength to help our children develop their potential and to become successful in school. That graduation day marked the end of elementary school and was ***our*** day of celebration!"

Their older son is now attending Amherst College, the country's top-ranked liberal arts college. Their younger son is now in high school and well into his college-bound plan. Mychal and Nina believe the strategies they have used, and continue to use with their sons, can be replicated by other parents. Countless children who are underachieving in school, and others who have been diagnosed as Hyperactive, having an Emotional/Behavioral Disorder (EBD), Learning Disabled (LD), or with Attention Deficit Disorder (ADD) have special talents and abilities, which can be channeled into long-term dreams and aspirations. All children can succeed in school as they journey along the road to richly rewarding lives and careers.

Eryn Davila is a parent and teacher. Ms. Davila is a fifth grade science teacher in the Dallas Independent School District. Ms. Davila believes that ensuring that all students experience school success requires that parents and teachers pay close attention to each child's developmental and learning style needs. Ms. Davila believes that if she can ensure that her students leave elementary school with a strong foundation, they will be well prepared to continue their growth through middle and high school in preparation for college and careers.

Serita Dodson is a third grade teacher in the Frisco Independent School District. Mrs. Dodson has taught kindergarten through third grade and believes that educating others is her calling. Her hope, through her contribution to this book, is that parents and teachers will become united around a common goal—the success of our children. Mrs. Dodson is currently pursuing a Masters in Administration degree at the Texas Woman's University. Mrs. Dodson lives in Texas and is married to Vincent Rois Dodson, Jr.

The activities and strategies that follow are intended to assist parents, grandparents, aunts, uncles, coaches, teachers, administrators, mentors, and counselors in helping children to succeed academically and develop socially throughout their elementary-through-high school experience. The activities and strategies expand upon the information contained in the book, *"Ten Steps to Helping Your Child Succeed in School."* The overview preceding each step refers the reader to pages in the book for more extensive reading. The *book* and *workbook* are part of Mychal Wynn's college-bound planning series, designed to assist parents and students in developing elementary-through-college plans.

Children We Care

Black, brown, red, yellow, and white,

    children of all colors with eyes so bright.

Given us in innocence, no burdens to bear.

    How can we say to you, "Children we care?"

How can we convince you that the love we give,

    is the most treasured possession of the life we live?

Toys, gifts, and trips to the zoo,

    are a very small part of the things that we do:

We love, nurture, and guide you along,

    laying the foundation from which to grow strong.

We teach you, protect you, and always demand,

    that in learning you simply do the best that you can.

And often the expectations that we have of you,

    are greater than you believe is the best you can do.

It's because in our lives we continue to see,

    that we rarely become the best we can be.

Our love and our lives, we always will share,

    forgive our mistakes, because "Children we care."

        — Mychal Wynn

Step 1

Get to Know Your Child

Getting to know your son or daughter is the first, and arguably, the most difficult step. As parents, we grew up in a different generation. We were taught different values than those constantly being directed at our children through today's music, movies, literature, and advertisements—not to mention the Internet. For many of us, family and church were the most important influences in our lives. For many of today's children, the influence of family is replaced by the powerful influences of peers and the media, i.e., television, radio, music, movies, videos, video games, and the Internet. The influence of church or spirituality in the lives of many children is no longer first or second, if on the list at all.

Ten Steps to Helping Your Child Succeed in School, p. 1

Step 1 Overview

Step 1 (pp. 1 - 48 in the book) clearly has more activities than any other step. Steps 2 through 10 build on what is learned through the activities in Step 1. Identifying the best schools, teachers, programs, and opportunities for children must account for the unique needs, aspirations, interests, and gifts of children.

While it is possible that a parent's learning style will be similar to that of their children, it is also possible that the two learning styles will be entirely different between parent and child and between any two children in the same family. Children learn by concentrating on, absorbing, using, and ultimately *processing* information. A child's learning style is the primary method by which he or she absorbs information. His or her intelligences represent the primary means by which he or she processes and uses that information. While parents and teachers can force a child to learn and to apply what he or she knows in the ways in which they do, they can only help a child to achieve his or her potential by helping him or her to further develop the natural processing styles that are uniquely his or her own.

Activity 1

Avoid Stereotypes and Generalizations

Objective

- Engage in a self-assessment of the stereotypes and generalizations that parents and teachers make regarding children and their behaviors.

- Identify common "slips of the tongue."

Overview

It is natural for us, as parents, to project our values, beliefs, personality, and ways of understanding things on to our children. However, by doing this we fail to "see"  our children in their own uniqueness, with their own values, beliefs, personality, and ways of understanding things. While they are our children, they are not born with our values, beliefs, or sense of right and wrong; and, they certainly may not have our personality or understand things in the ways in which we do. While we may teach and cultivate our values and beliefs, our children's personality and the ways in which they understand things is uniquely theirs. As parents, we must learn *how* to best help our children *learn* the values and develop the character we want them to have. To successfully teach our children, we must better understand the uniqueness of their personality and the ways in which they best learn.

Review the statements that follow regarding what we say to children, what we say about children, and how we explain the difficulties that children experience in learning and decision-making.

Things we say about children

Place a check next to those statements that you have made (or thought) in dealing with your children at home or students in the classroom.

❑ "Children today just don't have any respect for themselves or for anyone else."

❑ "It doesn't matter what you say, these kids never do what you tell them to do!"

❑ "These kids are failing because they are just lazy."

❑ "I don't know why we bother with trying new programs. If these kids just took responsibility and did their work, they would be fine. They just don't care."

❑ "You may as well be talking to yourself. He doesn't listen to anything that you say. "

❑ "Kids today think that they can get away with anything and their parents are just as bad!"

❑ "We are never going to make AYP [Annual Yearly Progress] with these kids. They don't care about school. They all want to become rappers and athletes."

❑ "I don't know why everyone keeps talking about college. These kids aren't college material."

❑ "These kids think that this is a baby sitting service."

❑ "You can't be nice to these children. They will see that as a sign of weakness and they will never do what you tell them to do."

❑ "These kids just want to play football. They don't want an education."

❑ "These kids have so many challenges that they have to overcome. If we can get them through high school and into a good job, that's about all that we can hope for."

❑ "These kids don't have any at-home support. Their parents don't care about education."

What other generalizations or stereotypes have you made, or have you heard other parents or teachers make in response to their frustrations in dealing with the attitudes and behaviors of their children or students?

_____

_____

_____

_____

_____

_____

_____

_____

_____

_____

_____

_____

_____

_____

_____

_____

Things we say to children

Place a check next to those statements that you have said (or thought) when you projected your childhood experiences on to your children.

- ❑ "I do not understand why you keep getting low grades in math; I never had problems with math."

- ❑ "No matter what my friends did, I knew that I had to focus first and foremost on getting my education."

- ❑ "When I was your age, I never did that!"

- ❑ "I would never have talked to my mother the way that you talk to me."

- ❑ "When I was in school, I always turned in my homework."

- ❑ "When I was in school, I would never have gotten sent to the office!"

- ❑ "There is no excuse for you to fail this class. If you just took responsibility and did your work, you would be fine. Failing is YOUR choice."

- ❑ "If you don't turn your work in on time, then you are choosing to get a zero. There is no excuse for forgetting to turn your work in."

- ❑ "You don't deserve another chance. When you get out into the real world, no one will give you a second chance. If you don't get your job done, then you are going to get fired."

- ❑ "This is ridiculous. If you would have studied, you would have gotten an 'A.' The truth is that you didn't study. There is no doubt about it!"

- ❑ "You failed that test because you didn't care. You just don't care about your future."

Mistake #1

We project our childhood experiences on to our children to explain their behaviors.

Ten Steps to Helping Your Child Succeed in School: Workbook © Mychal Wynn

What other statements have you made, or have you heard other parents or teachers say to children?

_____

_____

_____

_____

_____

_____

_____

_____

_____

_____

_____

_____

_____

_____

_____

_____

_____

_____

Things we say to explain the behaviors, successes, and failures of children

Place a check next to those statements that you have made (or thought) in which you explained a child's behavior through generalized assumptions, e.g., "You just can't talk to children today" or "Everyone knows that boys can't sit still."

❏ "You know how children are today."

❏ "He is just going through a phase; he will grow out of it."

❏ "He is hyperactive; he just cannot sit still."

❏ "She has a learning disability."

❏ "His attention span is so short; he just cannot concentrate."

❏ "She is not very good at math. I was not very good at math either."

❏ "He is just like his daddy!"

❏ "I don't think that college is right for him. No one in our family has ever gone to college."

❏ "He would do a lot better if he didn't have girls on his mind."

❏ "His sister is really smart, but you know that he is a boy and boys don't catch on to stuff as fast as girls do."

❏ "She would be a good student if it wasn't for those girls that she hangs around and that no good boyfriend."

Mistake #2

We rationalize our children's behaviors without getting to know our children.

Ten Steps to Helping Your Child Succeed in School: Workbook © Mychal Wynn

What other generalized assumptions have you made, or have you heard other parents or teachers make in explaining a child's behavior, successes, or failures?

_____

_____

_____

_____

_____

_____

_____

_____

_____

_____

_____

_____

_____

_____

_____

_____

_____

Activity 2

Quiz: What do I know about My Child (or Student)?

Objective

Engage in a self-assessment of what is currently known in regard to a child's learning styles, Multiple Intelligences, personality types, and academic strengths and weaknesses.

Overview

This activity begins the process of gathering information about your children or students. Just because parents live in the same household and see their children every day does not mean that they know their children. Despite common socioeconomic, cultural, ethnic, developmental, and gender characteristics, a classroom of 28 students is likely to have a wide range of learning styles, personality types, Multiple Intelligences, and academic strengths and weaknesses.

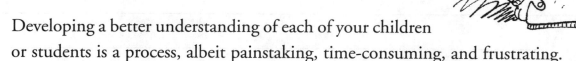

Developing a better understanding of each of your children or students is a process, albeit painstaking, time-consuming, and frustrating.

Identify one child or student and write his or her name on the following line:

Child's Name: _____

Regarding this student, as best as you can, attempt to answer the questions on the following pages: (Skip those questions or terms that you do not fully understand.)

1. *Of the eight intelligences (identified by Dr. Howard Gardner and commonly referred to as Multiple Intelligences), which are this child's dominant intelligences?*

    ❑ Verbal/Linguistic

    ❑ Logical/Mathematical

    ❑ Interpersonal

    ❑ Intrapersonal

    ❑ Visual/Spatial

    ❑ Musical/Rhythmic

    ❑ Bodily/Kinesthetic

    ❑ Naturalist

2. *Of the Myers-Briggs Personality Type Preferences, which are this child's dominant personality traits?*

    ❑ Introverted   ❑ Extraverted   (check one)

    ❑ Sensitive   ❑ Intuitive   (check one)

    ❑ Thinking   ❑ Feeling   (check one)

    ❑ Judging   ❑ Perceiving   (check one)

3. *Which is this child's dominant learning style category?*

    ❑ Analytic   ❑ Global

4. *How does this child appear to best understand?*

    ❑ Hearing   ❑ Seeing   ❑ Doing

5. What has been this child's best and worst learning situations in school?

_____

_____

_____

_____

6. What are this child's strengths, weaknesses, and intrinsic motivations?

_____

_____

_____

_____

7. How greatly is this child influenced by peer pressure?

_____

_____

_____

_____

8. What are this child's favorite hobbies, interests, subjects, and books?

_____

_____

_____

_____

9.   What are this child's proudest accomplishments and achievements?

_____

_____

_____

_____

_____

_____

_____

_____

10. What are this child's dreams and aspirations?

_____

_____

_____

_____

_____

_____

_____

_____

Gathering and understanding the information needed to answer each of these questions will help you, as a parent or teacher, to better understand how your child or student processes and applies knowledge; how to more effectively communicate with your child or student; how your child or student best learns; how to help your child or student make the connection between what he or she is learning in school and what he or she wants to achieve in life; and how to tap into the many areas of your child's or student's intrinsic motivation. The more you learn about your child or student, the more successful you will become at overcoming the inevitable challenges of parenting and teaching.

Activity 3

Personality Types— Who We Are

Objective

- Perform a personality type assessment for each child or student.

- Gain a better understanding of how personality type differences influence children's behaviors, responses to instructions, and classroom performance.

- Identify more effective methods of parenting and teaching differing personalities.

- Gather the necessary data to guide experimentation with various types of classroom grouping, teaming, and cultivating relationships with and between children.

Overview

The most important factor in your daughter's succeeding in school will be her personal relationships—the relationship between her and you; the relationship between her and her siblings; and the relationships between her and the teachers, staff, and students in her school.

Review the Personality Type tables and consider the following:

- Identify the personality traits that you demonstrate at work or in work-related situations as opposed to the personality traits you demonstrate around family and friends.

- Identify the personality traits demonstrated by your child at home as opposed to the personality traits demonstrated at school, in special interest or extracurricular activities, and with friends.

On the following Personality Type tables, adapted from the book, *Gifts Differing: Understanding Personality Type,* by Isabel Briggs Myers and Peter B. Myers, place a check next to those personality traits, which best describe you. Do the same for each of your children. The book, *A Middle School Plan for Students with College-Bound Dreams,* provides an in-depth student discussion in the areas of personality types, Multiple Intelligences, and learning styles.

[Note: The term Extravert is commonly referred to as Extrovert in contemporary literature on temperament. I prefer to use the term Extravert as was originally used in the Myers-Briggs Type Indicator.]

After completing the tables on the following pages, return here and make note of your personality type preferences and that of your child or student. Have your child or student complete the tables for himself or herself and compare your results. Learn more about personality type preferences through the many Internet resources that provide personality type testing tools and activities (Google "personality types").

Your Personality Type:

Your dominant personality traits are:
(check one on each line)

❏ (E) Extravert ❏ (I) Introvert
❏ (S) Sensitive ❏ (N) Intuitive
❏ (T) Thinking ❏ (F) Feeling
❏ (J) Judging ❏ (P) Perceiving

Child's Name: _____

This child's dominant personality traits are:
(check one on each line)

❏ (E) Extravert ❏ (I) Introvert
❏ (S) Sensitive ❏ (N) Intuitive
❏ (T) Thinking ❏ (F) Feeling
❏ (J) Judging ❏ (P) Perceiving

A child's personality type preferences are likely to change as he or she undergoes the many physical-emotional changes from infancy through adulthood. Parenting strategies must take into account the differences in the preschool, elementary, middle, and high school child.

Ten Steps to Helping Your Child Succeed in School, p. 18

Personality Types Table I

(E) Extravert (75% of population):

❑ I like variety, action, and working with others.

❑ I easily meet, get to know, talk to and socialize with others.

❑ I enjoy talking while working.

❑ I easily communicate my thoughts and ideas in lively, even loud discussions, where people frequently interrupt others.

❑ I frequently talk about things (often unrelated) as soon as they enter my mind, even if I occasionally interrupt others.

❑ Words that might describe me are: *Sociable, Interacting with others, Outgoing, Talkative, Lots of friends and relationships, Friendly*

(I) Introvert (25% of population):

❑ I like quiet, uninterrupted time for focusing and concentrating.

❑ I do not easily meet new people and sometimes have trouble remembering names and faces.

❑ I prefer to think about my ideas and talk after completing my work.

❑ I sometimes avoid sharing my thoughts, ideas, and opinions in large-group settings unless it is agreed that everyone has an opportunity to speak.

❑ If people interrupt me when I am sharing my thoughts, ideas, and opinions, I tend to stop talking and keep my thoughts to myself.

❑ Words that might describe me are: *Protective of my feelings, Territorial, Inwardly Focused, Internal, Serious, Intense, Small circle of friends*

This child is more of an: E   *or*   I   *(Circle One)*

    Ten Steps to Helping Your Child Succeed in School: Workbook © Mychal Wynn

Personality Types Table II

(S) Sensitive (75% of population):

❑ I prefer regular assignments and consistency.

❑ I prefer working through things step-by-step.

❑ I prefer to know exactly what needs to be done before starting a project.

❑ I am patient with routine details but I can be impatient when details become complicated.

❑ I prefer an established way of doing things and I get frustrated by changes.

❑ I feel good about what I already know and would prefer not to waste time experimenting with learning new ways of doing things.

❑ Words that might describe me are: *Experienced, Realistic, Hard worker, Down-to-earth, Focus on the facts, Practical, Sensible*

(N) Intuitive (25% of population):

❑ I like solving new problems.

❑ I prefer working on a variety of things.

❑ I do not like wasting time talking; just tell me what to do so that I can get started.

❑ I do not like working on repetitive work and find myself driven by inspiration.

❑ I am constantly thinking about how to redesign, improve, or change things.

❑ I like solving new problems and continually expanding my knowledge.

❑ Words that might describe me are: *Multi-tasking, Future, Focused, Speculate about the possibilities, Inspiration, Ingenious, Imaginative*

This child is more of a: S   or   N   (Circle One)

Personality Types Table III

(T) Thinking (50% of population):

❑ I do not usually show my feelings. I prefer dealing with facts rather than feelings.

❑ I prefer to know what you think rather than how you feel.

❑ I unintentionally hurt other people's feelings.

❑ I like analysis, order, figuring things out and being in charge.

❑ I prefer sharing my thoughts and ideas by focusing on the issues instead of on people and feelings.

❑ I tend to be analytical, focusing on thoughts and ideas instead of people.

❑ Words that might describe me are: *Objective, Principles, Policy, Laws, Firm, Impersonal, Justice, Focus on the problem, Standards, Analysis*

(F) Feeling (50% of population):

❑ I am concerned about other people's feelings and may overlook facts to avoid hurting someone's feelings.

❑ I prefer to know how people feel rather than what they think.

❑ I prefer harmony and avoid discussing controversial issues to avoid conflict.

❑ I do not handle personal conflicts well and may be upset long after an argument.

❑ I sometimes view constructive criticism as a personal attack.

❑ I am sympathetic to other people's feelings.

❑ Words that might describe me are: *Subjective, Caring, Humane, Understanding, Sympathetic, Harmonious, Appreciative*

This child is more of a: T   or   F   *(Circle One)*

Personality Types Table IV

(J) Judging (50% of population):

❑ I work best when I can plan my work and follow my plan.

❑ I like to reach closure. I want to complete projects, resolve issues, and move on.

❑ I do not take long to make up my mind.

❑ I am usually satisfied with my judgment or decision.

❑ After completing a project I am ready to move on to another.

❑ I do not like interruptions. Interruptions can cause me to lose my train of thought or forget some of the details.

❑ Words that might describe me are: *Settled, Decided, Fixed, Plan ahead, Closure, Decision-maker, Planner, Completed, Decisive, Wrap it up, Urgent, Deadline!, Get the show on the road*

(P) Perceiving (50% of population):

❑ I sometimes do not plan well.

❑ I sometimes work on projects without a clear plan and find myself frequently changing my mind.

❑ I sometimes leave things incomplete while I reconsider my choices.

❑ I sometimes find myself having trouble making decisions and find myself re-opening discussions or revisiting issues.

❑ I occasionally jump from project to project, leaving all open and incomplete.

❑ I do not mind interruptions.

❑ Words that might describe me are: *Pending, Gather more data, Flexible, Don't be in a hurry, Reconsider your decision, Tentative, Something will turn up, Let's wait and see, Are you sure?*

This child is more of a: J   or   P   (Circle One)

Extraverts and Introverts
in the Classroom

Essential to any reading method is the reassurance that letters stand for sounds and, therefore, a printed word shows the reader what it would sound like if it were spoken. The translation of sound-symbols is easiest for introverts with intuition. In first grade, the IN [Introversion plus Intuition] students are likely to be the quickest to catch on to the symbols and often are delighted with them. But the extravert children with sensing, the ES [Extravert plus Sensing] students, who make only minimal use of either intuition or introversion, may find the symbols so confusing that they become discouraged about the whole business of going to school. They may even decide, hopelessly or defiantly, that school is not for them.

Confusion about symbols is a very serious matter. Children of any type are doomed to flounder in school if they do not learn the meanings of the symbols by which language is written and must be read. They will be poor readers or non-readers, depending on the depth of their confusion. They will do badly on achievement tests and intelligence tests. They will probably be bored by what they do not understand and may well be humiliated because they do not understand it. They tend to drop out of school as soon as possible. Their failures may be blamed on low IQs or perhaps on emotional difficulty, whereas actually, the failures and the low IQ and the emotional difficulty could all result from one omission: nobody helped them, in the beginning, to learn the explicit meanings of the sound symbols.

Ten Steps to Helping Your Child Succeed in School, p. 30

Extraverts — Introverts Quick Guide

Extraverts Need:

Opportunities to talk.

Opportunities to participate in group activities.

Opportunities to talk while working.

No rules of engagement: let them talk, raise their voices, or even scream so that they can ensure that they are being heard.

Talk face to face. "Let's get this party going and get this show on the road."

Few safeguards. "If you talk about me, then I will talk about you back."

Has lots of friends, knows lots of people, and is invited to lots of parties.

No name tags. Know everyone's name and has lots of phone numbers.

Attention. Loves being in the mix and wants to participate in many activities.

Social time. When working in groups, will focus more on the social experience than on the work itself.

Free-flowing discussions. Does not mind interruptions. "I don't care if you interrupt me when I am talking, because I am going to interrupt you when you are talking."

Introverts Need:

Opportunities to read.

Opportunities for self reflection.

Opportunities to work alone, uninterrupted, even in isolation.

Clear rules of engagement: e.g., when do "I" get to speak and I want to ensure that everyone is listening when I have my turn to talk.

Personal space. "Don't get in my bubble. Take your time. There is no hurry. There is no need for stress."

Clearly stated and consistently enforced rules.

Has small group of friends and feels out of place at parties and large gatherings.

Name tags. Has difficulty remembering names.

Left alone. Does not like to participate in too many activities.

Work time. When working in groups, will focus more on the work than on the social experience.

Monitored discussions. Has difficulty speaking in public and in large-group settings. Is frustrated by interruptions. "If you do not want to hear what I have to say, then I will keep it to myself."

Activity 4

Multiple Intelligences— Identifying Gifts

Objective

- Perform a Multiple Intelligences assessment for yourself and for each child or student.

- Identify the intellectual gifts or areas of interest that can be nurtured and encouraged.

Overview

Each of us has, or can demonstrate, intelligence in at least eight ways and there may be many more. Sometimes when a person is good at a sport like basketball, we may consider him or her as being talented, but we are unlikely to view his or her basketball playing ability as being smart. "You got game!" not, "You got brains!" However, when a person masterfully dribbles a basketball or soccer ball, he or she is actually demonstrating highly developed *Bodily/Kinesthetic Intelligence*. This is the part of the human brain that controls body movement and hand-eye coordination.

The person who expertly illustrates comic book characters, cartoons, or puts together color-coordinated stylish outfits has highly developed *Visual/Spatial Intelligence*, not just drawing talent or an eye for fashions. The person who has a highly developed intuition in understanding animals and animal behaviors, camping, hiking, or surviving in the natural environment is highly developed in what is called the *Naturalist Intelligence*. There are many ways to demonstrate intelligence and many types of intelligences. No matter how much a child may excel in one subject or struggle in another, he or she is likely to experience both highly developed and weak areas of intelligence. In some subjects, he or she is likely to appear a genius and in other subjects, not very smart at all. Complete the Multiple Intelligences tables for yourself and for your child or student.

Multiple Intelligences

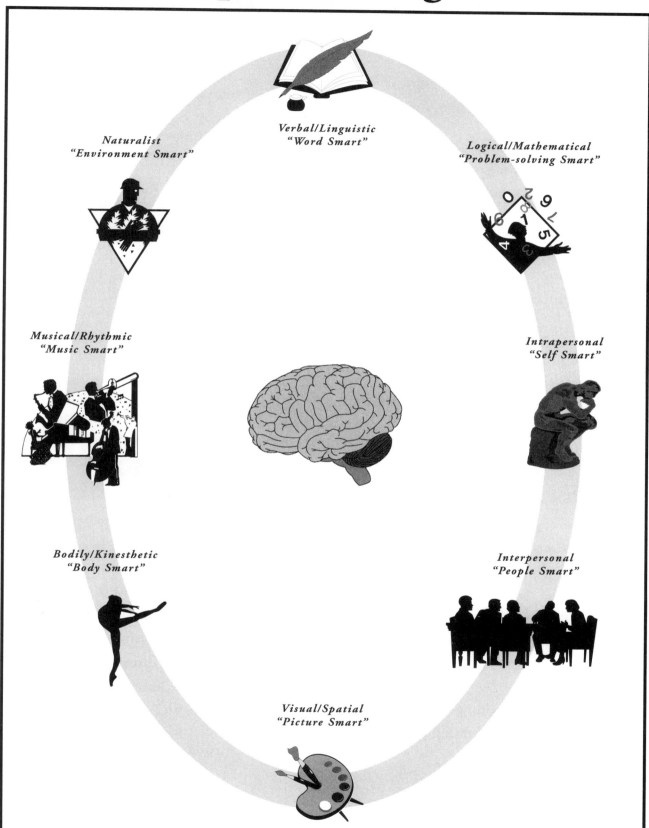

Verbal/Linguistic

_____ I enjoy reading

_____ I enjoy telling stories

_____ I enjoy creating stories, poetry, or raps

_____ I am good at writing about my thoughts or ideas

_____ I am good at talking about my thoughts or ideas

_____ I have a good understanding of things when there are written instructions

_____ I enjoy reading about my hobbies or interests (e.g., books, news articles, magazines)

_____ I remember things best when I have a list or by reading about them

_____ I enjoy word games like Scrabble or word puzzles

_____ When working in groups or on teams, I enjoy doing the research or writing the presentation

Logical/Mathematical

_____ I am good at problem-solving in subjects like math and science

_____ I enjoy doing experiments or figuring out complex problems

_____ I enjoy asking questions and figuring out how things work

_____ I believe that I have a logical mind and I am good at critical thinking

_____ I am good at developing plans

_____ I am good at organizing things into a step-by-step fashion

_____ I am good at gathering data or analyzing information

_____ I enjoy sharing my thoughts and ideas

_____ I enjoy math, problem-solving, or strategy games

_____ When working in groups or on teams I enjoy creating charts/graphs or organizing the presentation

Interpersonal

_____ I get along well with others

_____ I have good friendships

_____ I enjoy talking to or communicating with others

_____ I am good at understanding others

_____ I feel comfortable at parties and large gatherings of people

_____ I am good at organizing teams

_____ I am good at building relationships

_____ I am good at cooperating or collaborating with others

_____ I empathize with others and their feelings

_____ When working in groups or on teams, I enjoy working with my team members and prefer to reach a consensus on important decisions

Intrapersonal

_____ I am inwardly focused and self-directed

_____ I am good at being in touch with my feelings

_____ I enjoy concentrating on my thoughts

_____ I do not mind working alone

_____ I enjoy meditating and daydreaming

_____ I prefer self-directed projects

_____ I prefer to have my own space and move at my own pace

_____ I prefer to gather my thoughts before participating in group discussions

_____ I tend to have a small group of friends with whom I am really close

_____ When working in groups or on teams, I enjoy accepting tasks that I can work on independently

Visual/Spatial

_____ I am good at creating pictures in my mind

_____ I am good at drawing

_____ I enjoy creating models or designing things

_____ I have a good imagination

_____ I am good at choosing clothing or hair styles

_____ I prefer to see a picture or a diagram of how something works

_____ I am good at directions or reading maps

_____ I enjoy interior design

_____ I have a lot of creative ideas

_____ When working in groups or on teams, I do not mind being responsible for creating the cover and/or design or laying out the presentation

Bodily/Kinesthetic

_____ I am good at sports

_____ I enjoy dancing

_____ I am good at building things or working with my hands

_____ I am good at creating new gymnastics, martial arts, or boxing movements

_____ I am good at roller skating

_____ I enjoy riding bicycles, skiing, or snowboarding

_____ I have good body coordination

_____ I find it easy learning new sports or dance moves

_____ I enjoy putting things together and repairing things

_____ When working in groups or on teams, I enjoy presenting a demonstration through dance, gymnastics, or other ways in which I can use my body

Musical/Rhythmic

_____ I enjoy singing

_____ I enjoy playing an instrument

_____ I easily remember tunes, songs, or lyrics

_____ I am good at keeping a beat or remembering a melody

_____ I enjoy writing songs or creating musical compositions

_____ I am good at picking up sounds

_____ I tend to hum or tap a beat when I am working or thinking

_____ I am good at mixing music

_____ I like music playing while I study

_____ When working in groups or on teams, I enjoy creating theme songs or selecting background music

Naturalist

_____ I am good at hiking, camping, fishing, and living in the environment

_____ I am good at understanding and working with animals

_____ I enjoy working or being outdoors

_____ I would enjoy survivalist competitions

_____ I have a good feeling of what is going on around me

_____ I would enjoy living or working on a farm

_____ I am good at identifying insects or tracking animals

_____ I notice cloud and rock formations

_____ I can feel changes in weather patterns

_____ When working in groups or on teams, I enjoy creating the stage arrangements or building a backdrop

Activity 5

Multiple Intelligences Study Tips

Objective

- Develop study strategies by viewing each child's intelligences within the context of learning styles.

- Develop a Multiple Intelligences approach to at-home study.

Verbal/Linguistic

When you think of this intelligence within the context of a learning style, think of someone who loves to talk and write. Children who learn best this way like to complete their work by writing down information or talking about it to someone.

Debate it: Engage in a debate of assigned reading, homework, area of interest, or of an area that is currently being studied such as state capitals, math facts, or historical facts. Take any area that your child is currently studying in school, have a family discussion and let everyone give his or her opinion. When you have finished, have your child explain to you what he or she learned.

Prove it: This approach is also good with math problems. After solving a math problem, have your child tell you why it is right or wrong. This will help your child clearly and fully understand the steps that he or she took in solving the problem. Key questions to guide your discussion include, "What was the problem? What were the steps that you took to solve the problem? What is the answer? What steps did you take to check your answer?"

Spell it: In the primary grades, students come home with spelling words to learn each week. Later, in middle school, students will begin learning their SAT/ACT vocabulary. When your child comes home with the words, have him or her say the words aloud, and then use the words in a riddle, rap, poem, or in a sentence. Your child can also write a poem or short story using the words. Another good activity is to use a composition notebook to begin his or her own dictionary of words. Encourage your child to look for opportunities to use the words as part of his or her daily conversations.

Logical/Mathematical

When you think of this intelligence within the context of a learning style, think of someone who enjoys categorizing, classifying, or working with abstract patterns/relationships.

Vocabulary Terms: To assist this type of learner in expanding his or her vocabulary, consider having your child create his or her own vocabulary crossword puzzle. The clues would be the definitions and the answers would be the vocabulary terms. He or she could also take this activity to school to share with the class. Games like Scrabble™ are also good challenges for this type of learner.

Intrapersonal

When you think of this intelligence within the context of a learning style, think of someone who enjoys working alone, through individualized projects, self-paced instruction, or having his or her own space.

Check and Review: Since this type of learner often prefers to work alone, it is important for you to check and review his or her work when finished. Ask him or her questions on how he or she arrived at the answers, or if he or she prefers to show you by writing how he or she arrived at the answers, encourage him or her to show you in this way. It is important to remember that your child will eventually have a job one day and that he or she will have to communicate verbally with co-workers. This is a skill that you can nurture and develop over time.

Interpersonal

When you think of this intelligence within the context of a learning style, think of someone who enjoys sharing, comparing, relating, cooperating, and interviewing.

Study Groups: This type of learner loves to interact with others. A great way for you to be involved in the school setting and to meet other parents would be to host an at-home study group or study group party. You can also turn this into a lock-in, where students spend the night and discuss different projects and topics that are going on at school. Encourage this type of learner to participate in after-school clubs and extracurricular activities such as student government, Beta Club, Speech and Debate, and the National Honor Society.

Visual/Spatial

When you think of this intelligence within the context of a learning style, think of someone who enjoys visualizing, or working with colors and pictures.

Spelling ideas: Have this type of learner write his or her spelling words in big block letters. This way he or she can write the words in a fun and exciting way. He or she will also be able to visualize writing the words the next time he or she writes them.

Math: While completing math problems, have him or her write the sign in different colors. For example, if he or she is writing 3 + 3 = 6, he or she may want to do the numbers in one color and the signs in another. This approach gives him or her just a different way to see the problem.

Below, and on the following page, are illustrations by our older son, who is now attending Amherst College. As a child, he picked up his passion for art by watching and mimicking his older cousin, who had a passion for drawing comic book heroes. As a result of at-home nurturing, through "How To" videos and books; the nurturing of teachers throughout middle and high school; and experiences in after-school programs and summer camps; his *passion* for drawing evolved into a *talent* for drawing. We feel blessed as parents to have noticed his passion for drawing, and then to have nurtured his intelligence for drawing.

Ten Steps to Helping Your Child Succeed in School: Workbook © Mychal Wynn

Bodily/Kinesthetic

When you think of this intelligence within the context of a learning style, think of someone who enjoys touching, moving, processing knowledge through bodily sensations or by doing.

A bodily/kinesthetic learner wants to be active while working or studying, so the typical sit-down-at-the-table atmosphere may not work best for him or her. If your child is a bodily/kinesthetic learner, the following examples may benefit him or her to learn the material at home.

Manipulatives: Use some sort of manipulative to problem solve. If he or she has math problems that he or she needs to work on, you can use objects (forks, crayons, blocks, etc.) at home to help him or her sort out the problem. For example, if he or she has a math sheet of multiplication problems, you can use crayons, toothpicks, jacks, pennies, or noodles to show the problem. Line them up so that he or she can see why 3 x 9 = 27. This way will give him or her the opportunity to move around or use his or her hands while learning.

Another approach would be to take a walk, go for a run, or ride a bicycle while reciting the multiplication tables.

Acting out: If he or she has assigned reading, you can assess his or her understanding of the material by having him or her act out what he or she has read. He or she can set up a play in the living room and show you what he or she learned from the book. He or she may even use stuffed animals, pillows, statues, or other artifacts to set up the scene and represent different characters. He or she may even assign you a role and tell you what to do and say. This is a fun and interactive way!

Musical/Rhythmic

When you think of this intelligence within the context of a learning style, think of someone who enjoys rhythm, melodies, and music. This type of learner remembers or processes information best through rhythm, melodies, and music.

Sing it: Do you ever wonder why your child can so easily remember a song that he or she listened to on the radio, but then cannot remember how to spell a word that he or she has been learning all week? Singing the information may be the solution to that problem. While trying to learn the weekly spelling words, use the beat from his or her favorite song or have him or her put the words together in a rap or song. When he or she takes the test, he or she can sing the song or recite the rap in his or her head without disturbing others. Even those of us who are not musical/rhythmic learners can remember singing our "ABCs."

Rap it: While working on writing an essay for school, when your child is completing the pre-writing activity, he or she may benefit from rapping it while writing it on paper. For those students who are already dreaming of becoming the next big rapper, this approach may be the key to helping them get the pencil flowing while writing.

Naturalist

When you think of this intelligence within the context of a learning style, think of someone who enjoys being outdoors or in the natural environment using all of the senses.

Outside day: Provide opportunities for your child can go outside to complete his or her homework. Or, provide a work area in a backyard, on a front porch, or on a patio to stimulate his or her senses in a way that helps him or her to process and remember information more easily. The environmental sounds of birds, crickets, frogs, or automobiles driving by may help him or her to make connections between facts and remember information more easily.

Nurture Your Child's Multiple Intelligences

Verbal/Linguistic

- ❏ Read a book and write a report
- ❏ Write in a journal
- ❏ Write a letter, a story, or a poem
- ❏ Tell a story, write a newsletter
- ❏ Recite a poem, story, or rap
- ❏ Participate in Spelling Bees
- ❏ Memorize the state capitals
- ❏ Public speaking
- ❏ Practice debating a point of view

Visual/Spatial

- ❏ Read maps, charts
- ❏ Put together puzzles
- ❏ Use your imagination and write a story
- ❏ Design your room
- ❏ Practice photography, graphic design
- ❏ Write and illustrate stories
- ❏ Create flyers, brochures, comic strip

Bodily/Kinesthetic

- ❏ Play sports, martial arts, roller skate
- ❏ Create dance routines
- ❏ Build something
- ❏ Learn to use a lacrosse stick
- ❏ Learn sign language

Musical/Rhythmic

- ❏ Sing songs, join a choir
- ❏ Write music, play an instrument
- ❏ Write a song or rap
- ❏ Identify notes and chords in music
- ❏ Identify songs and artists
- ❏ Identify differences in musical themes

Logical/Mathematical

- ❏ Work on logic problems
- ❏ Do math word problems
- ❏ Plan a daily schedule
- ❏ Plan a trip
- ❏ Compute the total as you shop
- ❏ Organize your subject binders
- ❏ Plan your summer vacation
- ❏ Become a math tutor
- ❏ Research a science project

Interpersonal

- ❏ Organize a family outing
- ❏ Plan a party
- ❏ Host a get-together for friends
- ❏ Join a group or club
- ❏ Become a conflict mediator
- ❏ Keep track of how long you can go without complaining

Intrapersonal

- ❏ Set goals, develop personal projects
- ❏ Pursue an interest
- ❏ Coordinate family share time
- ❏ Keep a journal
- ❏ Take time to think about thinking

Naturalist

- ❏ Write a haiku
- ❏ Learn the constellations
- ❏ Make a list of your favorite plants, animals, and places to visit
- ❏ Plan a camping or fishing trip
- ❏ Learn to tie knots

Activity 6

Multiple Intelligences Grouping

Objective

- Observe students in applying varying intelligences toward problem solving.

- Experiment in various cooperative grouping strategies and methodologies.

Overview

Talk to students about each of the areas of Multiple Intelligences and have them select what they believe to be their dominant intelligence. Group students according to like intelligences, i.e., Visual/Spatial, Logical/Mathematical, Interpersonal, etc. Assign to each group tasks that rely on their dominant intelligence. For example, the Visual/Spatial group can design a bulletin board; the Logical/Mathematical group can design classroom procedures; the Interpersonal group can brainstorm on activities to build relationships; the Musical/Rhythmic group can develop a rap or identify theme songs for the classroom or for different units of study.

The next step would be to allow the members of each group to present a class project through their dominant intelligence, e.g., PowerPoint presentation, rap, skit, etc.

Home Activity

Experiment with Multiple Intelligences grouping for home projects. Visual/Spatial family members can focus on design elements. Logical/Mathematical family members can focus on creating budgets and developing schedules. Interpersonal family members can focus on ensuring that family members maintain healthy relationships and feel appreciated. Bodily/Kinesthetic family members, working with their hands, can focus on building things and using their bodies. Working together and appreciating each family member's unique gifts and talents can help to build strong families where all gifts are valued and appreciated.

Activity 7

Turn Your Home into An Eagle's Nest

Objective

Use the story of *The Eagles who Thought They were Chickens* as an inspiring lesson for your children to spread their wings and soar toward their dreams.

Overview

This book is perfect for opening up the school year and for cultivating a positive classroom climate and culture. After reading the book aloud to the class, or having students read the book and write essays about the attitudes of the eagles, chickens, and roosters in the story, you can go right into your behavioral expectations for the year. This story has a lot of history that students can learn and provides a moral that is a great life-lesson. The behaviors exhibited by the chickens, roosters, and eagles in the story provide many parallels to what may happen in the classroom, at

recess, while moving between classes, or when a substitute teacher is in the classroom. It provides a great tool for teaching and reinforcing behavioral expectations and for encouraging students to dream and set goals.

Place your students into Multiple Intelligence groups and ask them to represent the moral of the story in their own way.

Verbal/Linguistic

These learners can retell one part of the story where the moral is most significant.

Logical/Mathematical

These learners can review the story together and make a chart showing 5 causes and effects in the story. They should be able to sequentially show the events of the story using their chart. They could also determine a solution to name-calling and bullying at school and at home.

Interpersonal

These learners work so well together that they can design a skit highlighting the conflict of the story and its resolution and present the skit to the class.

Intrapersonal

These learners can illustrate and explain the differences between the chickens and the eagles and relate those differences to their own lives. How are you treated differently and how do you handle that different treatment?

Bodily/Kinesthetic

After reading the story, have these learners role play both a section of the book and how students behave at the school. The class can compare the differences.

Musical/Rhythmic

Musical learners can work together and make up a song that relates to the book and their feelings about the book.

Visual/Spatial

Group these students together and have them create a mural to hang in the school, decorate a bulletin board, or illustrate the story.

Naturalist

These learners should go outside and find materials that they can use to depict a scene from the book. Once they have created the scene, they can write a poem that they can read to the class.

Activity 8

Learning Styles

21 Learning-Style Elements:

Environmental:

1. Sound
2. Light
3. Temperature
4. Design

Emotional:

5. Motivation
6. Persistence
7. Responsibility
8. Structure

Sociological:

9. Self
10. Pair
11. Peers
12. Team
13. Adult
14. Varied

Physical:

15. Perceptual
16. Intake
17. Time
18. Mobility

Psychological:

19. Global/Analytic
20. Hemisphericity
21. Impulsive/Reflective

Objective

- Perform a learning-styles assessment for each child or student.

- Gain a better understanding of environmental, emotional, sociological, physiological, and psychological variables that influence a child's ability to acquire, process, retain, and apply information.

- Identify the intellectual gifts or areas of interest that can be nurtured and encouraged.

Overview

[The information for this activity is taken from the book, *A Middle School Plan for Students with College-Bound Dreams*.]

Most people have learning-style preferences, but individuals' preferences differ significantly. Learning Styles reflect an individual's personal reactions to each of 21 elements *when concentrating on new and difficult academic knowledge or skills*. To capitalize on a student's learning style, you need to be aware of his or her:

- reactions to the immediate classroom environment—background noise such as music and talking versus silence, bright light versus soft lighting, warm versus cool temperatures, and formal (e.g., desk and chair), versus informal (e.g., bed, floor, or bean bag) seating;

- emotional state—motivated, persistent, responsible, and able to exercise control over the learning environment versus a classroom setting that is largely controlled by the teacher with teacher-imposed deadlines, rules, etc.;

- social preferences for learning—working alone, with friends or classmates, with an adult, or in a variety of ways as opposed to teacher-determined patterns or routines;

- physiological preferences—perceptual strengths (auditory, visual, tactual, or kinesthetic strengths), time-of-day energy levels, intake (snacking while concentrating), or mobility needs.

The belief that there is one best way for students to learn is a widely held misconception. Many teachers attribute student failure to lack of motivation, lack of interest, poor study habits, or simply lack of the intellectual capacity to succeed in certain subject areas. However, the reality is that people remember new and difficult information through different perceptual modalities. For those of you who are thinking, "Perceptual what?" it means that people learn differently. Parents of  children who learn visually are oftentimes guilty of saying, "In one ear–out the other." They wonder why their children are not successful in remembering or following verbal instructions. Such children may simply be visual learners. They do not learn best and struggle to successfully follow instructions when they are "told" the steps. They need to "see" the steps.

Review each of the following 21 Learning-Style Elements and check those elements or influences that most reflect your child or student. Check the preferences that either the child or student has indicated or that you have observed.

Environmental Elements:

1. Sound

    ❑ quiet   ❑ background noise (e.g., TV, radio, voices)

2. Light

    ❑ bright   ❑ subtle or dim

3. Temperature

    ❑ cooler   ❑ warmer

4. Design

    ❑ formal (e.g., desk, table, chair)   ❑ informal (e.g., bed, sofa, floor)

Emotional Elements:

5. Motivation

    ❑ self motivated   ❑ requires extrinsic motivation (e.g., rewards, threats)

6. Persistence

    ❑ will work through problems independently   ❑ needs monitoring and assistance

7. Responsibility

    ❑ can responsibly follow instructions   ❑ needs help

8. Structure

    ❑ requires structure and clear rules   ❑ requires open structure and the flexibility to use own approach

Sociological Elements:

9. Self

    ❑ comfortable working independently ❑ more comfortable working
    with others

10. Pair

    ❑ prefers that teacher chooses partner ❑ prefers to choose own partner

11. Peers

    ❑ prefers working alone ❑ prefers working with peers

12. Team

    ❑ works well on teams ❑ struggles on teams or with teamwork

13. Adult

    ❑ requires little supervision ❑ requires adult supervision

14. Varied

    ❑ prefers consistent grouping ❑ prefers variety of situations and choices

Physiological Elements:

15. Perceptual

    ❑ listening ❑ seeing ❑ touching ❑ moving around

16. Intake

    ❑ prefers to eat while working ❑ prefers to eat after working

17. Time

    ❑ learns best during the morning ❑ afternoon ❑ evening

18. Mobility

    ❑ prefers to move around ❑ prefers to sit still

Psychological Elements:

19. Global/Analytic

    ❑ prefers stories, humor, pictures

    ❑ prefers step-by-step or fact-by-fact

20. Hemisphericity

    ❑ prefers rational, step-by-step approaches (left brain processing)

    ❑ prefers artistic or creative approaches (right brain processing)

21. Impulsive/Reflective

    ❑ prefers quick decisions

    ❑ prefers slow decisions and time to think through the details and possibilities

Many Different Ways of Learning

Ten Steps to Helping Your Child Succeed in School: Workbook © Mychal Wynn

Learning Styles Table

Global

The greatest challenge in teaching global learners is not to bore them. They appear to learn best through stories, humor, and pictures. Following are some of the situations in which global learners appear most comfortable:

- Prefer hearing a story or watching a movie or play.

- Prefer noise while working (music, TV, or talking).

- Prefer to work in groups where they talk while they work.

- Appear to learn best from the interaction with other children (particularly with similar interests and talents) rather than from direct adult supervision and instruction.

- Prefer to eat while working.

- Prefer informal seating for learning, e.g., bean bag, pillow, rocking chair, bed, carpet, etc.

- Prefer working on several things at a time with breaks in between.

- Remember most of what is said without taking notes. Learn best when "told" what to do.

Ten Steps to Helping Your Child Succeed in School, p. 43

Learning Styles Table (cont.)

Analytic

Analytic learners appear to learn most easily when information is introduced step-by-step or fact-by-fact. Following are some of the situations in which analytic learners appear most comfortable:

- Prefer things to be quiet.

- Prefer to work in groups where they talk after they work.

- Prefer to eat after working.

- Prefer bright lights and formal seating like a desk, table, or chair.

- Prefer working on one thing at a time and completing tasks.

- Prefer taking notes while the teacher is talking.

- Learn best when instructions are written.

Additional Learning Styles

- Auditory: Learns best by hearing.

- Kinesthetic: Learns best by doing.

- Tactile: Learns best by touching.

- Visual: Learns best by seeing.

Ten Steps to Helping Your Child Succeed in School, p. 44

Activity 9

Global vs. Analytical Thinkers

Objective

- Identify global versus analytical approaches to problem solving.

- Identify ways of presenting information and better supporting student learning.

Overview

This activity requires parents and teachers to consciously observe student learning. As problems are assigned, it is important to allow students sufficient freedom and independence in determining their preferred problem-solving methods and approaches. The focus of this activity is not to assist students in correctly solving problems, but to observe their preferred approaches to solving problems.

Identify a series of problems. Experiment with word problems printed in a textbook, word problems projected onto the board via an overhead projector, problems that are verbally communicated to students, and problems that are visually represented or presented through flow charts or diagrams.

Discussion

"I would like for you to solve the following problem using whatever means, problem-solving strategies, or approaches that you feel work best for you. Whether you prefer to draw pictures, take notes, discuss the problem with classmates, work alone, stand up, walk around, or refer to other books and materials, you are free to work in the ways in which you learn best. Feel free to come up and speak with me if you need further instructions.

I have indicated the time that everyone must stop, whether you have solved the problem or not. I have an activity box in the front of the classroom that has books, games, puzzles, and other activities in which you may be interested. After you have completed your work, you may come up and choose another activity to quietly do at your desk until the time has expired."

Things to look for

Global learners may respond to the problem using pictures, look at the general idea of the problem first and then go back to look for details. They may ask questions like, "Why are we doing this? Can I do it later? I cannot work while it is this quiet? Can I work with another student?"

Analytical learners prefer taking a linear approach to figuring out the problem. They will show you a step-by-step process of learning. They will solve the problem based on logic, facts and common sense. They need visual reinforcement, but do not rely on it. They may ask questions like, "Is this going to be in the test? When is this due? Can you check my work? Is this how you do it? What do you think of this?"

Track Student Achievement Data

Carefully performing Step 1 should assist any parent or teacher in helping a child to become a successful learner. Ultimately, the parent's or teacher's effectiveness in performing Step 1 will be reflected in the child's achievement level. The books, *A Middle School Plan for Students with College-Bound Dreams: Workbook [Wynn, 2006]* and *A High School Plan for Students with College-Bound Dreams: Workbook [Wynn, 2005]* contain worksheets for tracking student grades, test scores, extracurricular activity involvement, etc. No matter where you are in your child's college planning, you must measure your success at performing Step 1 by tracking your child's achievement data throughout his or her school-age years, i.e., preschool through high school.

Set aside a folder for filing your child's report cards, standardized test scores, and ability assessments. Consider keeping and storing your child's school work if you have the space or at least storing a representative sampling of your child's school work within each subject area as your child progresses from preschool through high school.

Step 2

Identify the Best School

D o not spend all of your time looking for schools with the highest test scores or high schools with the highest graduation rates and largest percentage of students who go on to college without spending time understanding your child. Being the highest-ranked school does not guarantee that a school will be the best school for your child or guarantee that your child will get the best teachers for her unique needs, ambitions, dreams, or aspirations.

Ten Steps to Helping Your Child Succeed in School, p. 49

Step 2 Overview

Step 2 (pp. 49 - 90 in the book) provides activities to assist parents in researching schools and programs. Some parents are fortunate to have many choices of schools—public, magnet, private, faith-based, charter, or university laboratory schools. Other parents may be limited to the zoned school within their local school district. Subsequently, whether you have a choice in determining the **school** that would best work for your child or the **teacher** who you believe would work best for your child, you must work with administrators, counselors, and support staff within the school to help them to best work *with* your child.

You have a responsibility to your child to get to know everything you can about the school and the people in it. Always remember that good schools welcome parental involvement. Good teachers welcome the opportunity to become partners with parents in their child's education. Good teachers invite people to look at how and what they teach because good teachers provide good classroom instruction and you can see learning taking place.

Activity 10
Research Schools and Programs

Objective

- Engage in the process of identifying schools, programs, and opportunities to nurture a child's gifts, abilities, and areas of interest.

- Identify how to take optimum advantage of the opportunities offered in a child's zoned schools or within available school choices.

- Identify parental involvement and volunteer opportunities to best support the efforts of a child's school.

Overview

School choice will vary widely from multiple choices, e.g., public, private, magnet, charter, etc., to few choices to no choices. Even when parents have little or no choice of schools, they will find multiple choices of programs, levels of course work, and extracurricular opportunities within the school. The activities in this section will assist in identifying the best schools when there are choices, the best programs within a school, and sensitizing parents and teachers to the need for developing strategies to expose children to enrichment opportunities beyond those offered by the local school or school district.

(Refer to pages 57-58 in the book for a listing of web sites that provide helpful information regarding school performance, student demographics, etc., to assist in your research.)

Test your knowledge of your state and local school system:

Write the grade level(s) next to the tests that are given in your school:

ITBS: _____ *CTBS:* _____ *NAEP:* _____

State Tests: _____ *SAT:* _____ *ACT:* _____

PSAT: _____ *EOG:* _____ *EOCT:* _____

EOC: _____ *CRCT:* _____ *Other:* _____

High School Exit Exam(s): *Y or N*

If yes, make note of the grade that it is given next to the subject:

English/Language Arts: _____ *Math:* _____ *Science:* _____ *Social Studies:* _____

GPA calculated on a: *4-point scale:* _____ *5-point scale:* _____ *Numeric:* _____

Additional weight (indicate weight) given to: *Honors:* _____ *AP:* _____ *IB:* _____

Classes that can be taken in middle school for high school credit:

_____

_____

Middle school clubs, organizations, and extracurricular activities that have a minimum academic requirement:

_____

_____

_____

High school clubs, organizations, and extracurricular activities that have a minimum academic requirement:

_____

_____

_____

_____

Ten Steps to Helping Your Child Succeed in School: Workbook © Mychal Wynn

Course enrollment policy for your school district:

Honors:	*Open*	*Recommendation*	*Grade in Prerequisite Class*	*Other*
Pre-AP:	*Open*	*Recommendation*	*Grade in Prerequisite Class*	*Other*
AP:	*Open*	*Recommendation*	*Grade in Prerequisite Class*	*Other*
IB:	*Open*	*Recommendation*	*Grade in Prerequisite Class*	*Other*
Joint Enrollment	*Open*	*Recommendation*	*Grade in Prerequisite Class*	*Other*

Criteria for identifying academically gifted children: _____

_____

Additional criteria:

❑ *Teacher Recommendation* ❑ *Counselor Recommendation* ❑ *Grades*

❑ *Psychological Assessment* ❑ *Prerequisite Courses* ❑ *Other*

_____

Indicate the earliest grade that gifted identification of students occurs: _____

Indicate the programs that gifted children are referred to:

❑ Duke TIP (www.tip.duke.edu/) (Grade level(s): _____)

❑ Johns Hopkins University Center for Talented Youth (CTY) (www.cty.jhu.edu/)

   (Grade level(s): _____)

❑ Other: _____ (Grade level(s): _____)

Minimum requirements for acceptance into the state university system in your state:

_____

_____

Does your state university system offer state scholarships, and, if so, what is the qualifying criteria and how much of the tuition, room, board, and books would the program cover?

_____

_____

Activity 11

What Is Your Vision?

Objective

- Clarifying the level of achievement you envision for your child.

- Clarifying the values and beliefs that are consistent with the level of achievement you envision for your child.

- Identifying at-home routines, enrichment programs, and before- and after-school programs to assist your child in reaching the level of achievement that you envision.

Overview

Review and discuss the question on the following page. Is your vision clear? Have you clearly and consistently communicated your values and beliefs to your child? Have you enrolled your child into programs that reinforce your values and beliefs, and, that will assist your child in achieving the level of success that you envision? Are your at-home, before- and after-school routines consistent with your vision? Are you celebrating your child's successes and reinforcing your values and beliefs?

Discuss such questions with other parents and with those persons who have supervisory responsibilities for your children, e.g., teachers, counselors, coaches, administrators, mentors, relatives, and neighbors.

Home

1. *Develop your vision, i.e., what type of adult do you want your child to become? Make a list of words that you envision being used to describe your son or daughter as an adult, e.g., spiritual, responsible, polite, kind, compassionate, trustworthy, honest, diligent, determined, resilient, persistent, persevering, confident, self-motivated, respectable, intelligent, etc. (Refer to page 67 in the book for more questions pertaining to the process of clarifying your vision.)*

_____

_____

_____

_____

_____

_____

_____

_____

_____

_____

_____

_____

_____

_____

_____

_____

_____

Activity 12

What Is the School's Vision?

Objective

- Identifying the level of achievement the school appears to envision for students.

- Identifying whether the values and beliefs promoted within the school community are consistent with the level of achievement envisioned for students.

- Identifying whether the type of routines, enrichment programs, and before- and after-school programs are consistent with assisting students in reaching the level of achievement envisioned.

Overview

Parent involvement, staff development, school improvement planning teams, the local school council, and grade-level teams should review and discuss the questions on the following page. Has the school clearly communicated its vision? Has the vision clearly and consistently communicated school-wide values and beliefs to staff, students, and families? Have students been exposed to programs that reinforce school-wide  values and beliefs, and, that will assist students in achieving the level of success envisioned? Has the school developed the appropriate customs, rituals, and programs necessary to reinforce school-wide values and beliefs?

School

1. Are the school's mission, vision, and beliefs verbally affirmed and visually displayed?

    If "Yes," how are they affirmed and where are they displayed?

    _____

    _____

    _____

2. Do classroom and program practices reinforce the "4Cs" (caring, clarity, commitment, and consistency) and consistently communicate the values and beliefs of the school's vision and guiding principles?

    If "Yes," describe how they are practiced by your child's teachers:

    _____

    _____

    _____

3. Are the school's values and beliefs reinforced through instructional activities (language arts, performances, reading, writing, classroom discussions, assemblies, etc.) and through visual imagery (cups, flags, buttons, T-shirts, bumper stickers, etc.)?

    If "Yes," describe how they are promoted and reinforced throughout the school community:

    _____

    _____

    _____

(Refer to page 70 in the book for further questions pertaining to the school's vision.)

Activity 13

What Is the Teacher's Vision?

Objective

- Identifying the level of achievement envisioned for students by teachers.

- Identifying the values and beliefs that are consistent with the level of achievement envisioned by teachers.

- Identifying the type of routines, enrichment programs, support materials, and extra credit opportunities needed to assist students in reaching the level of achievement envisioned by teachers.

Overview

Grade-level meetings and parent-teacher conferences should be used to review and discuss the questions on the following page. Clearly and consistently communicating the teacher's vision for student achievement to  parents and students is an important component for creating a positive and high-performing classroom climate and culture. Identifying opportunities to encourage, support, and inspire student effort provide important strategies to support high levels of student achievement.

Classroom

1. Is the teacher's vision for student achievement clearly defined, verbally affirmed, and visually displayed within the classroom?

    If "Yes," how is the vision affirmed and where is the vision displayed?

    _____

    _____

    _____

2. Has the teacher developed a consistent set of classroom procedures, rewards, and consequences to reinforce the values and beliefs?

    If "Yes," how effective are they with children in the classroom?

    _____

    _____

    _____

3. Does the teacher appear to foster student collaboration through effective grouping of students, e.g., personality types, Multiple Intelligences, and learning styles, to help communicate and reinforce the values and beliefs of the classroom?

    If "Yes," how has your child responded to these types of grouping strategies?

    _____

    _____

    _____

(Refer to page 73 in the book for further questions pertaining to the classroom vision.)

Activity 14

What are Your Non-negotiables?

Objective

- Considering the unique needs, talents, and abilities identified in Step 1, clarify the non-negotiable issues that you are looking for in a school.

- Utilize web-based and local resources to assist in your research efforts.

Overview

Even when parents have limited school choices, parents must be aware of the options, opportunities, and obstacles that they are likely to experience within their child's school.

Questions that may be considered non-negotiables:

Is the school safe?
Does the school offer sports?
Does the school offer a music program?
Does the school offer a visual or theater arts program?
What are the school's test scores?
How effectively does the school provide for students with special needs?
Am I allowed to visit my child's classroom? If so how often?
Does the school encourage volunteers?
Does the school provide parent training or seminars?
Is student diversity valued and recognized?
How long are the class periods and how often does my child get to attend recess?
What is the balance between academics and social activities?
How effectively does the school and teachers communicate with parents?
Does the school offer before- or after-school programs?
What type of technology will my child be exposed to?
How does the school encourage and support student achievement?
What mechanisms are used to provide ongoing monitoring of student academic performance?

Ten Steps to Helping Your Child Succeed in School: Workbook © Mychal Wynn

Non-negotiables

As a parent or guardian, you have standards that are important for your child. While searching for the school that will best meet your child's needs, write down non-negotiables. Below is a checklist that will assist you. Your needs may change as your child enters different developmental stages (i.e., toddler, preteen, teenager) and school settings (i.e., preschool, elementary, middle, high school). After you have checked the most important factors, rank them. Ask yourself, "Are these realistic? Are they in the best interest of my child? Are they consistent with the vision that I have of the level and type of education I want for my child?"

	Negotiable (Yes/No)	Importance (1, 2, 3)
Sports		
Music		
Arts (Visual or Performing)		
Test Scores		
Local or State Rank		
Special Ed. Programs		
Talented & Gifted Programs		
Parent Involvement		
Inviting Environment		
Enrichment Opportunities		
Safety		
College Prep Support, Encouragement, and Course Work		
Academic Reputation		
Athletic Reputation		
Student Diversity		
Staff Diversity		
Tutoring and Student Support Services		
Technology		
Counseling/Psychological Support Services		
Socially Nurturing		
After-school Programs		

1 = Very Important, 2 = Important, 3 = Not Very Important

Activity 15

Parent Checklist and School Assessment

Objective

Provide a checklist for monitoring the information that you have researched.

Overview

When you have decided on the "best" school for your child by weighing your non-negotiables, you are ready to start your school file. This file ideally should be started in preschool or kindergarten and continually updated through your child's elementary,  middle, and high school years. Depending on your child's current grade you may want to begin gathering the information and begin your college planning as outlined in the books, *A Middle School Plan for Students with College-Bound Dreams* and *A High School Plan for Students with College-Bound Dreams*. In addition to your school file, your college planning activities will result in boxes of information.

Use the following as a handy checklist for identifying information that you have gathered from your school and program research.

Check those areas where you have gathered information thus far:

Information pertaining to your child

❑ Learning styles
❑ Multiple Intelligences data
❑ Personality type profile
❑ Strengths, weaknesses, and personal assessment
❑ Report cards, standardized tests, and ability assessments

Ten Steps to Helping Your Child Succeed in School: Workbook © Mychal Wynn

Information pertaining to your child's teachers

❑ Teaching style

❑ Multiple Intelligences instructional approaches

❑ Personality type profile

❑ Strengths, weaknesses, and personal assessment, e.g., will accept late assignments, allows make-up opportunities for low test/quiz grades, has open lines of communication with parents, etc.

Information pertaining to the school

❑ School Improvement Plan

❑ State School Report Card

❑ School's mission, vision, and core values

❑ School's web site, address, phone numbers, etc.

❑ Names and contact information for the principal, office staff, teachers, counselors, etc.

❑ School's newsletters and local news articles

❑ Student achievement and enrollment data

❑ Extracurricular activities, student organizations, and enrichment opportunities

❑ Course catalog (usually available for middle and high schools)

❑ Important dates, e.g., yearly calendar, school holidays, testing dates, report card dates, and registration dates

Information pertaining to the school district

❑ District Improvement Plan

❑ District Report Card

❑ District's mission, vision, and core values

❑ District web site, address, phone numbers, etc.

❑ Name and contact information for superintendent and school board representatives

❑ Performance of the schools in your child's cluster of schools, i.e., elementary, middle, and high school

❑ Types of testing by grade level, e.g., ITBS, EOG, high school exit exams, etc.

Elementary School: _____

Principal: _____

Phone: _____ FAX _____

Web site: _____

Student Population: _____ Asian: _____ Black _____ Hispanic _____

Multi-Racial _____ Native American _____ White _____ Other _____

Academic reputation: Excellent   Good   Average   Poor   Awful

Safety reputation: Excellent   Good   Average   Poor   Awful

Diversity: Excellent   Good   Average   Poor   Awful

Percentage of children of same race as your child: _____

Programs or activities that meet your child's needs, expands his or her interests, or provides important academic or enrichment opportunities:

_____

_____

_____

_____

_____

_____

_____

_____

_____

Middle School: _____

Principal: _____

Phone: _____ FAX _____

Web site: _____

Student Population: _____ Asian: _____ Black _____ Hispanic _____

Multi-Racial _____ Native American _____ White _____ Other _____

Academic reputation: Excellent   Good   Average   Poor   Awful

Safety reputation: Excellent   Good   Average   Poor   Awful

Diversity: Excellent   Good   Average   Poor   Awful

Percentage of children of same race as your child: _____

Programs or activities that meet your child's needs, expands his or her interests, or provides important academic or enrichment opportunities:

_____

_____

_____

_____

_____

_____

_____

_____

_____

High School: _____

Principal: _____

Phone: _____ FAX _____

Web site: _____

Student Population: _____ Asian: _____ Black _____ Hispanic _____

Multi-Racial _____ Native American _____ White _____ Other _____

Academic reputation:	Excellent	Good	Average	Poor	Awful
Safety reputation:	Excellent	Good	Average	Poor	Awful
Diversity:	Excellent	Good	Average	Poor	Awful

Percentage of children of same race as your child: _____

Programs or activities that meet your child's needs, expands his or her interests, or provides important academic or enrichment opportunities:

_____

_____

_____

_____

_____

_____

_____

_____

Activity 16

What Is My Role (parent)?

Objective

- Engage in a self-assessment of your role as the parent in ensuring the education of your child.

- Identify some of the at-home support and routines that will help your child to be a successful learner.

Overview

Creating a positive and supportive home environment is critical to preparing a child for school success. The all-important home-school partnership requires that parents accept a role, which in turn, is supported by the staff and classroom teachers at your child's school.

Consider some of the following committees and volunteer opportunities and check those areas where you are currently, or would consider becoming involved:

- ❏ PTA/PTSA ❏ School Advisory Counsel ❏ Booster Club

- ❏ Campus Improvement Committee ❏ Classroom Volunteer

- ❏ Front Office Volunteer ❏ Tutor ❏ Assist with special event

- ❏ Chaperone ❏ Guest Speaker ❏ Start club

- ❏ Donations (e.g., money, supplies) ❏ Start a parent support group

- ❏ Assist with physical improvements (e.g., paint, build trophy case, plant garden, decorate)

Activity 17

Get To Know Other Families

Objective

Consciously develop relationships with other families.

Overview

Some parents by their very nature have outgoing personalities. They easily meet and develop relationships with other families each school year. They routinely volunteer to serve on the PTA/PTSA, in booster clubs, or volunteer in their child's classroom. However, other parents and students find developing relationships with other students and families more difficult. This activity provides a set of steps for parents and students to consciously work toward building relationships with other students and families.

Parent reflection: "How can I build relationships with other families as a means of helping my child to experience a positive school year?" As children, many parents experienced growing up in communities where people knew one another and watched out for one another's children. Many school communities today are quite different. It is not uncommon for students to live in different neighborhoods and for parents to have little contact with families across neighborhood boundaries. Differences aside, building relationships with other families is important in assisting teachers in creating a positive classroom experience for all students. Beginning with the first school event, e.g., Meet and Greet, Open House, Registration, Opening of the football season, etc., set a goal to meet one new family at each school or classroom event.

Undoubtedly, the easiest way to meet other families is to volunteer at the school, at a sporting event, to chaperone a field trip, or to be introduced to other families by a friend who is already involved or well known within the school community. The steps on the following page provide additional opportunities to meet other parents.

Ten Steps to Helping Your Child Succeed in School: Workbook © Mychal Wynn

Consider the following steps as a means of breaking the ice and building relationships:

1. *Wear a T-shirt as a means of initiating a conversation, e.g., school T-shirt, your alma mater, local sports team, or local college.*

2. *Introduce yourself to families with common interests, e.g., children with the same teacher or coach, children involved in similar activities, children you have seen at places outside school, e.g., sporting events, church, community programs, parks and recreation.*

3. *Identify at least one parent or family to exchange information with for each of your child's classes, teachers, and activities.*

Class or activity: _____

Name: _____

Phone: _____

E-mail: _____

Class or activity: _____

Name: _____

Phone: _____

E-mail: _____

Class or activity: _____

Name: _____

Phone: _____

E-mail: _____

Class or activity: _____

Name: _____

Phone: _____

E-mail: _____

Class or activity: _____

A Curious Child

A tug on your arm,
  what could it be?
A child wants to know,
  how deep is the sea?
Don't try to ignore it,
  it's already begun.
The next question is,
  how hot is the sun?
It won't do any good,
  to pause for a sigh.
Before you can answer,
  how high is the sky?
Why are mountains so high
  and valleys so low?
Why are cheetahs so fast
  and turtles so slow?
Why do bees make honey?
  How do worms make silk?
Why do chickens lay eggs?
  How do cows give milk?
Before you can answer,
  a child question's again:
Why do we use dollars,
  the Japanese use yen?
We must never forget
  that in years gone by,
How we used to question
  and others would sigh;
Yet if they answered each question
  with a chuckle and grin,
It would prompt our curiosity
  to question again.
We must nurture the brilliance
  of the inquisitive child;
No matter how many questions
  let's just answer and smile.

— *Mychal Wynn*

Step 3

Develop a Plan

N ow that you have gathered information about your child and your child's school, what is your plan? Simply, what do you want your child to learn, experience, and be exposed to this school year? (You cannot simply say, "I want my child to learn as much as he or she can!")

Ten Steps to Helping Your Child Succeed in School, p. 91

Step 3 Overview

Step 3 (pp. 91 - 107 in the book) involves developing a plan for each of your children. This will require that you give careful thought to the unique gifts, talents, interests, and challenges facing each of your children. Subsequently, you must develop an idea of what *you* want your child to learn, experience, and be exposed to during this school year? (You cannot simply say, "I want my child to learn as much as he or she can!")

Be specific:

- *Do you want your child to learn more math, science, reading, writing, social studies, art, music, or social skills?*

- *Do you want your child to learn computer graphics, computer programming, web page design, architecture, fashion design, cosmetology, culinary arts, or construction?*

- *Do you want your child to learn about the stock market, the Internet, investments, or entrepreneurship?*

- *Do you want your child to learn how to be more independent?*

Activity 18

What Do You Want
Your Child (or Students) To Learn?

Objective

- Identify areas of talent or skill development.

- Identify weaknesses to be strengthened.

Overview

Do not rely on the school to determine the complete scope of what your child needs to know. Use whatever school authorities suggest as a guide. Keep in mind that the school's curriculum is designed to help students achieve minimum proficiency standards established by the State Department of Education. Most students can soar beyond the minimum proficiency standards when we tap their passion for learning. While other students may be ready to learn simple addition, your child may be ready to learn algebra. While other students may be set to read chapter books, your child's focus may need to be classical literature. While other students may still be dealing with grammar and sentence structure, your child may be ready for writing novels or publishing books of poetry.

After reviewing the student performance data on the following pages, identify the areas in which you would like for your child to focus more during the current school year.

States and school districts use a variety of assessment measures for evaluating student achievement and comparing student performance. On a national level, student performance on the National Assessment of Educational Progress (NAEP) (as indicated below) provides a clear picture that many children are languishing behind by the fourth grade, and are still far behind four years later in the eighth grade.

No matter which student group your child falls into, as his or her parent, you must take effective steps toward early intervention and pay close attention to his or her test scores as he or she progresses through each grade. Without early intervention, children who lag behind in student performance during the primary and middle school years are the least likely students to be prepared to enroll into rigorous high school classes, advanced math, or advanced science—all of which provide the best preparation for college success.

Students who perform well in a rigorous high school curriculum significantly increase their readiness to perform well on the SAT and ACT college admissions examinations (see p. 72).

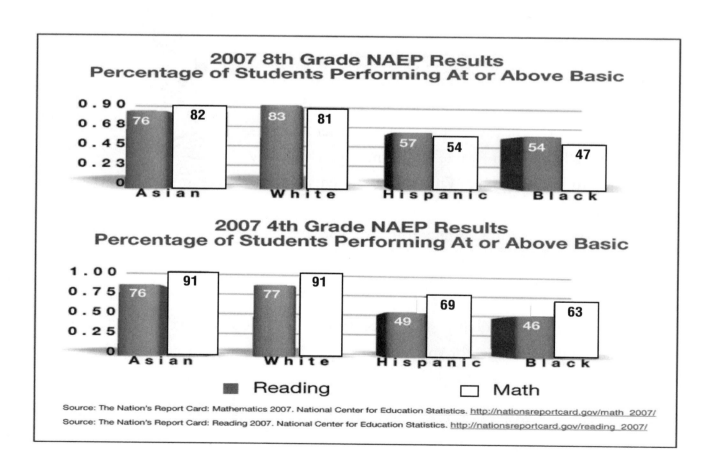

Ten Steps to Helping Your Child Succeed in School: Workbook © Mychal Wynn

2005 NAEP High School Transcript Study

Curriculum	Asian	White	Hispanic	Black
Rigorous Curriculum	22%	11%	8%	6%
Advanced Math	62%	46%	28%	29%
Advanced Science or Physics	62%	46%	34%	32%
6-Year College Grad Rates	65.4%	59.5%	47.0%	40.5%

Note: These percentages only represent the transcripts of those students who actually graduated from high school.

The Nation's Report Card: America's High School graduates, Results from the 2005 NAEP High School Transcript Study. (2007). National Center for Education Statistics. Washington, DC: U.S. Department of Education.

Carey, K. (2005). *One Step from the Finish Line: Higher College Graduation Rates are Within Our Reach.* Washington, DC: Education Trust.

AP Exam Performance in U.S. Public Schools by the Class of 2006 During Their High School Years

| | Exam Scores for Total Exams Taken | | | | | | |
Race	5	4	3	2	1	Average Score	Total Exams
White	136,847	222,629	293,619	247,565	145,930	2.96	1,046,590
Asian	42,635	51,122	58,779	51,033	38,123	3.04	241,692
Hispanic	21,475	29,365	41,140	48,988	63,141	2.50	204,113
Black	2,733	7,128	15,349	27,426	41,920	1.96	94,556

Advanced Placement Report to the Nation (p. 84). (2007). The College Board.

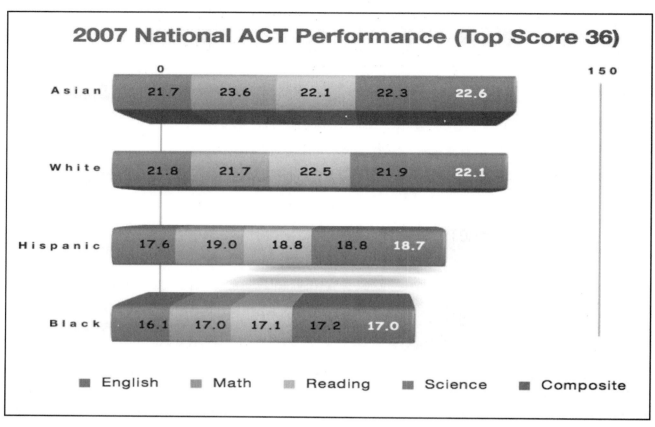

2007 National ACT Performance (Top Score 36)

	English	Math	Reading	Science	Composite
Asian	21.7	23.6	22.1	22.3	22.6
White	21.8	21.7	22.5	21.9	22.1
Hispanic	17.6	19.0	18.8	18.8	18.7
Black	16.1	17.0	17.1	17.2	17.0

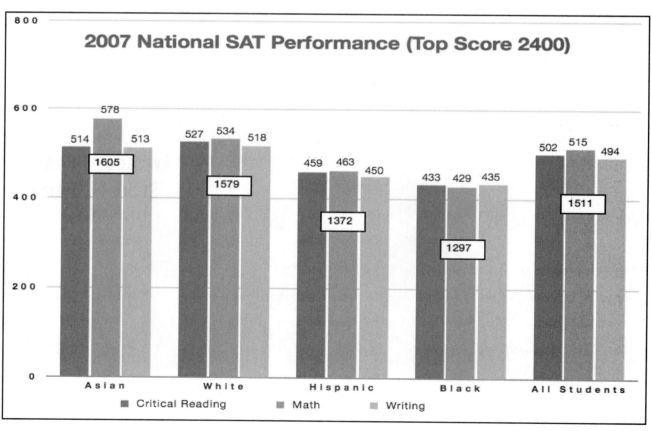

2007 National SAT Performance (Top Score 2400)

	Critical Reading	Math	Writing	Total
Asian	514	578	513	1605
White	527	534	518	1579
Hispanic	459	463	450	1372
Black	433	429	435	1297
All Students	502	515	494	1511

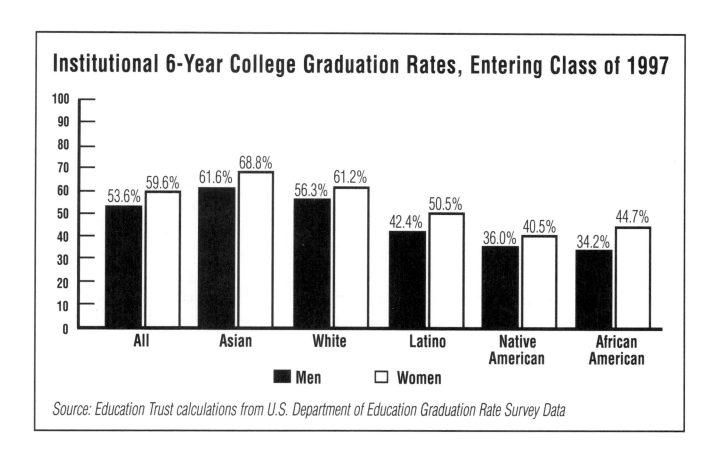

Institutional 6-Year College Graduation Rates, Entering Class of 1997

	All	Asian	White	Latino	Native American	African American
Men	53.6%	61.6%	56.3%	42.4%	36.0%	34.2%
Women	59.6%	68.8%	61.2%	50.5%	40.5%	44.7%

■ Men ☐ Women

Source: Education Trust calculations from U.S. Department of Education Graduation Rate Survey Data

As you review student performance on the SAT and ACT examinations, there is a clear correlation between the level of course work, i.e., higher-level math and science, the type of courses taken, e.g., honors, AP, and IB, student performance in such classes, and students' SAT and ACT scores.

You must clearly communicate your vision and academic expectations to both your child and to your child's teachers and counselors. While some students are self-motivated, most require collaboration between home and school to ensure that they are enrolled in the right classes and that they have the necessary support and monitoring of their achievement levels to be successful in elementary school through high school and prepared to successfully follow their college/career dreams and aspirations.

Check those areas in which you would like for your child to learn more during the current school year.

Academic

- ❏ Math
- ❏ Science
- ❏ Critical Thinking
- ❏ Social Studies
- ❏ Writing
- ❏ Study Skills
- ❏ Organization
- ❏ Foreign Language
- ❏ Research
- ❏ Reading

Creative

- ❏ Theater
- ❏ Music
- ❏ Singing
- ❏ Acting
- ❏ Band
- ❏ Writing
- ❏ Speaking
- ❏ Cheerleading
- ❏ Gymnastics
- ❏ Art
- ❏ Sports _____

Special Interest

- ❏ Fashion
- ❏ Cosmetology
- ❏ Entrepreneurship
- ❏ Trade
- ❏ Tourism
- ❏ Technology
- ❏ Medicine
- ❏ Government
- ❏ Automotive
- ❏ Aviation
- ❏ ROTC
- ❏ Color Guard
- ❏ Leadership
- ❏ Engineering
- ❏ Law
- ❏ Design
- ❏ Architecture
- ❏ Community Service
- ❏ Internship
- ❏ Teaching
- ❏ Investments
- ❏ Computers
- ❏ Model Building
- ❏ Culinary Arts
- ❏ Tutoring

Personal Development

- ❏ Social Skills
- ❏ Leadership
- ❏ Self Control
- ❏ Organization
- ❏ Writing
- ❏ Integrity
- ❏ Citizenship
- ❏ Responsibility
- ❏ Teamwork
- ❏ Respect
- ❏ Initiative
- ❏ Coaching
- ❏ Time Management
- ❏ Creativity
- ❏ Speaking

Other

_____

_____

_____

_____

Summer	In School	After School	Community	**Program Name**	Identify the summer, in-school, after-school, and community programs that will assist your child in increasing academic achievement or other personal development.

Activity 19

Look Beyond Labels— Identify Gifts

Objective

- Identify a child's gifts and talents.

- Avoid stereotyping children.

Overview

Within many school communities, children are generally defined by labels—Mentally Handicapped, Learning Disabled, Emotionally Disturbed, Behavioral Disorder, Attention Deficit Disorder, or Academically Gifted. Many parents reaffirm such labels:

"My son is hyperactive."

"My daughter is LD."

"My son is not doing well in school because he is ADD."

"My child is in the Gifted Program."

We must never forget that children are a continuous work-in-progress. We must be particularly careful not to allow labels to determine the scope of our children's dreams or influence the amount of thought and effort we put into developing the needed plans for our children to pursue their dreams. We must never stop looking for the interests, gifts, potential and possibilities in children.

Review the areas listed on the following page. Place a check next to those areas where your child has gifts, talents, and abilities. Compare your answers to those in the previous activity. Ensure that the programs that you identify will assist your child in both overcoming weaknesses and developing his or her gifts.

Place a check next to those areas where your child has gifts, talents, and abilities.

Academic

- ❏ Math
- ❏ Science
- ❏ Critical Thinking
- ❏ Social Studies
- ❏ Writing
- ❏ Study Skills
- ❏ Organization
- ❏ Foreign Language
- ❏ Research
- ❏ Reading

Creative

- ❏ Theater
- ❏ Music
- ❏ Singing
- ❏ Acting
- ❏ Band
- ❏ Writing
- ❏ Speaking
- ❏ Cheerleading
- ❏ Gymnastics
- ❏ Art
- ❏ Sports _____

Special Interest

- ❏ Fashion
- ❏ Cosmetology
- ❏ Entrepreneurship
- ❏ Trade
- ❏ Tourism
- ❏ Technology
- ❏ Medicine
- ❏ Government
- ❏ Automotive
- ❏ Aviation
- ❏ ROTC
- ❏ Color Guard
- ❏ Leadership
- ❏ Engineering
- ❏ Law
- ❏ Design
- ❏ Architecture
- ❏ Community Service
- ❏ Internship
- ❏ Teaching
- ❏ Investments
- ❏ Computers
- ❏ Model Building
- ❏ Culinary Arts
- ❏ Tutoring

Personal Development

- ❏ Social Skills
- ❏ Leadership
- ❏ Self Control
- ❏ Organization
- ❏ Writing
- ❏ Integrity
- ❏ Citizenship
- ❏ Responsibility
- ❏ Teamwork
- ❏ Respect
- ❏ Initiative
- ❏ Coaching
- ❏ Time Management
- ❏ Creativity
- ❏ Speaking

Other

_____

_____

_____

_____

Activity 20

What Am I Celebrating?

Objective

- Engage in a self-assessment of the successes that you are celebrating.

- Ensure that what you celebrate is consistent with the expectations that you communicate.

Overview

Encouraging and celebrating your child's success will be one of the most important components of your plan. Your plan will also require exposing your child to new opportunities and experiences and helping your child experience success each school year. Good grades, high test scores, positive experiences, and opportunities to expand and share his or her interest will all provide your child with the feeling of success, the feeling of being capable.

What Did You Celebrate Last School Year?

Complete this activity by writing down everything that you celebrated at home or that was celebrated at your child's school during the previous school year. Allow yourself one minute to write down everything that you celebrated for or with your child:

_____

_____

_____

_____

_____

_____

_____

_____

_____

_____

_____

_____

_____

_____

_____

_____

_____

Activity 21

Making Connections —Developing Your Plan

Objective

To ensure that your plan focuses on encouraging, developing, and celebrating your child's unique gifts, talents, and successes.

Overview

Each school year you must decide what you want your child to know, what sports or activities you want him or her to do, and what programs, opportunities, and people to whom you would like him or her exposed to. While some children will eagerly provide you with a list of programs, camps, or sports that interest them, other children will require that you are more hands-on in guiding their way.

After considering what you learned from the previous activities, consider the following questions:

1. Do you currently have balance in assisting your child in overcoming his or her weaknesses and in expanding his or her gifts and talents?

2. Have you clearly communicated your academic achievement, personal development, and creative expression expectations?

3. Are you sufficiently celebrating your child's achievements?

Place a check next to those areas that you believe your child, if sufficiently coached or encouraged, may increase his or her chances for college admissions and be considered for college scholarship opportunities.

Academic

❏ Math ❏ Science ❏ Critical Thinking ❏ Social Studies ❏ Writing
❏ Study Skills ❏ Organization ❏ Foreign Language ❏ Research ❏ Reading

Creative

❏ Theater ❏ Music ❏ Singing ❏ Acting ❏ Band
❏ Writing ❏ Speaking ❏ Cheerleading ❏ Gymnastics ❏ Art
❏ Sports _____

Special Interest

❏ Fashion ❏ Cosmetology ❏ Entrepreneurship ❏ Trade ❏ Tourism
❏ Technology ❏ Medicine ❏ Government ❏ Automotive ❏ Aviation
❏ ROTC ❏ Color Guard ❏ Leadership ❏ Engineering ❏ Law
❏ Design ❏ Architecture ❏ Community Service ❏ Internship ❏ Teaching
❏ Investments ❏ Computers ❏ Model Building ❏ Culinary Arts ❏ Tutoring

Personal Development

❏ Social Skills ❏ Leadership ❏ Self Control ❏ Organization ❏ Writing
❏ Integrity ❏ Citizenship ❏ Responsibility ❏ Teamwork ❏ Respect
❏ Initiative ❏ Coaching ❏ Time Management ❏ Creativity ❏ Speaking

Other

_____

_____

_____

Creating your child's plan will be a continuing work-in-progress. Over the course of the school year, refer to your answers to activities 19 to 21 and organize your plan into the following areas:

- Long-term dreams and aspirations: e.g., family; career; travel; special skills; exposure; politics; entrepreneurship, etc.

- Short- and long-term goals: e.g., honor roll; National Honor Society; advanced or honors classes; standardized test scores; college; becoming proficient in a foreign language; academic or athletic scholarships; art, music or other type of special instruction, etc.

- Things you would like for your child to learn or be exposed to.

- Ways in which you would like your child to grow personally: e.g., become more responsible; develop better study habits; increase his or her math scores; become more organized, etc.

- Clubs, extracurricular, special interest, special programs, or after-school activities you would like your child to experience.

- Classes, course work, extracurricular activities, and community service that you believe will make your child a competitive candidate for college admissions. When planning for college, keep in mind that the requirements for admissions into state universities, out-of-state public universities, private universities, and junior or community colleges will vary widely—so too, will the cost of tuition, room, and board.

- Refer to the books, *A Middle School Plan for Students with College-Bound Dreams,* and *A High School Plan for Students with College-Bound Dreams* to ensure that your child is on track to take the most rigorous classes in which he or she is capable of succeeding.

Ten Steps to Helping Your Child Succeed in School: Workbook © Mychal Wynn

Step 4

Meet the Staff

When you enter the front office, meet, greet, and shake hands with all of the office staff. As soon as possible, write down the names of each person in the front office, however, do not stop there. Get to know as many of the people in the school as possible—cafeteria workers, custodians, coaches, administrators, safety officers, and the school bus driver. My wife and I try to develop relationships with all of the adults who are there to look out for and look after our sons.

Ten Steps to Helping Your Child Succeed in School, p. 109

Step 4 Overview

Step 4 (pp. 108 - 115 in the book) involves building relationships with school personnel. Begin by contacting the school and requesting a meeting with the principal or counselor. Prior to the meeting, give him or her a copy of your plan and the background information pertaining to your child, e.g., learning style, Multiple Intelligences, best learning situations, personality type, etc. The purpose of this meeting is to ask the principal or counselor for his or her input as to how the school can best help you to help your child to become successful. How you prepare for this meeting will help to shape perceptions about you as a parent. Keep in mind that this meeting is about relationship building. You want to develop a relationship, and shape perceptions that say:

- I am concerned about my child's success in school.

- I have invested time gathering information that will be helpful in the placement of my child.

- I want to be an involved parent.

Activity 22

Meet and Greet

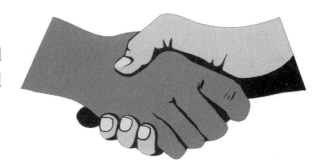

Objective

Ensure that you know the people who will be influencing your child during the school year.

Overview

When your child is in a new school or one that he or she has previously attended, it is important to know who works in the school. You never know when you may need to contact a particular teacher or the secretary. Use the space below to write down names.

Name	Phone or E-mail
Principal	
Principal's Secretary	
Assistant Principal	
Assistant Principal	
Assistant Principal	
Front Office Staff	

_____

_____

_____

_____

_____

	Name	**Phone or E-mail**

Attendance Clerk _____

(Attendance records, records if your child is transferring to a new school)

Nurse _____

(Medical problems your child may have, child's shot records)

Diagnostician _____

(Questions on any testing the school might give, definitions of test)

Counselor_____

(Discuss problems that your child may have and get suggestions on how to solve problems at home)

Teachers

Homeroom _____

Math _____

Social Studies _____

Science _____

Language Arts _____

Foreign Language _____

Reading _____

P.E./Health _____

Computer/Technology_____

Art _____

Music _____

| **Name** | **Phone or E-mail** |

Librarian/Media Specialist _____

Cafeteria Workers _____

_____

_____

Custodians/Engineers _____

_____

_____

_____

Safety Officers _____

_____

_____

Coaches _____

_____

_____

_____

Others _____

_____

_____

_____

Activity 23

Sharing What You Know about Your Child

Objective

Provide important information about your child to his or her teachers, counselor, coaches, and administrators.

Overview

As close as possible to the beginning of the school year, or as soon as your child enters a new school, give the principal and the classroom teacher(s) all of the information that you gathered during Step 1 and any other information you feel will help your child get off to a good start to the school year or to make a smooth transition into a new school. Following is some of the information that will be helpful in assisting teachers to get to know your child and to better understand how to assist your child in being successful.

Student's Name _____

Parent(s) Name(s) _____

Student's Age _____ Personality Type _____

Best Learning Situations _____

_____

_____

Worst Learning Situations _____

_____

_____

Learning Style Preferences _____

_____

_____

Things That Motivate My Child _____

_____

_____

Things That Upset My Child _____

_____

_____

My Child's Major Strengths _____

_____

_____

My Child's Major Weaknesses _____

_____

_____

How to Best Communicate With Me _____

_____

_____

Best Time(s) to Communicate With Me _____

_____

_____

Dream-Builder's Affirmation

I will look beyond the problems
> *to the solutions.*
I will look beyond the obstacles
> *to the opportunities.*
I will look beyond the impossible
> *to the possibilities.*
I will look beyond the darkness
> *to the light.*
When others doubt,
> *I will provide courage and inspiration;*
When others quit,
> *I will demonstrate strength*
> *and determination.*
I cannot do everything,
> *but I can do something.*
What I can do, I must do;
> *what I must do, I will.*

> — *Mychal Wynn*

Step 5

Be Visible

Let your child know that you may show up anytime and unannounced. Look in on him or her and observe the classroom dynamics and your child's participation. Elementary school students love for parents to come to their classroom or to have lunch with them. Middle school students *hate* for parents to come to their school. High school students *want to die* whenever their parent comes to their school. Remember, you are the parent and you are responsible for doing what is in the best interest of your child. From my experiences of being involved in hundreds of middle and high schools throughout America; one of the biggest problems is the absence of parents. The behaviors of students and staff alike are positively affected by parents being in the building. The best thing that could happen to create safer and higher academically achieving middle and high schools would be for parents to become involved on a day-to-day basis in schools. This truly would be a rebirth of the village.

Ten Steps to Helping Your Child Succeed in School, p. 116

Step 5 Overview

Step 5 (pp. 116 - 121 in the book) involves determining the level of involvement that you will have in your child's school so that teachers and school personnel recognize you as an involved parent and know that there is someone advocating for your child. Beginning with the first day of school, go to your child's school as often as you can. Just show up and walk around. Remember, this is your school. Find out what the school's policy is for visiting classrooms. Follow the policy and visit your child's classrooms. Be sure to meet and greet the principal, teachers, and office staff by name. If you have a hard time remembering names, make notes about each person and associate his or her name with physical features. "Mr. Jones, tall! Ms. Smith, red hair. Mrs. Johnson, reminds me of my mother!"

If you can, go to PTA/PTSA meetings, performances, workshops, or other meetings held at the school. Take advantage of any opportunity to get involved in the school. Even if your schedule does not permit you to attend all of the school meetings and functions, it is important for teachers to see you around the school.

Activity 24

Getting Involved

Objective

Determine the best or most practical way for you to become involved in your child's school.

Overview

There is one global reality to parental involvement—when parents are involved, every school becomes a better school! Subsequently, making your child's school a better school will benefit not only your child, but countless other children and families. This activity will assist you in matching your gifts and talents to volunteer opportunities.

Following are common volunteer opportunities and ideas for matching your gifts, talents, schedule, and personality to those opportunities. Check the ones that are most practical for your involvement, given your work and daily obligations.

PTA/PTSA

❏ Officer   ❏ Committee   ❏ School Opening   ❏ Fundraising   ❏ Speaker

Make note of the meeting dates, times, and locations.

Month	Date	Time	Location
August			
September			
October			
November			
January			
February			
March			
April			
May			
June			

What I Can Do for My Child's School

❏ **Art:** I can paint a mural in the school, help maintain bulletin boards, maintain the school display cases, assist with art projects in the classroom, or provide interior design ideas ❏ **Music:** I can donate instruments or support music instruction ❏ **Photographer:** I can take pictures for the yearbook ❏ **Award Ceremonies:** I can plan and coordinate student award and staff recognition ceremonies ❏ **Fundraising:** I can organize fundraising events, solicit donations from local businesses, or apply for grants ❏ **Woodwork:** I can build cabinets and trophy cases ❏ **Business:** I can volunteer to talk about my career during career week, join the career week planning committee, invite friends and associates to become guest speakers, encourage my business or workplace to become a business partner, identify potential business partners in my community or where I worship ❏ **Seamstress:** I can sew costumes ❏ **Tax Accountant:** I can prepare tax returns ❏ **Strategic Planning:** I can volunteer to serve on school improvement planning teams ❏ **Athletics:** I can volunteer for field day, donate athletic equipment, take a walk with teachers, participate in parent-staff athletic competitions, join a booster club, get equipment donations from parks and recreation departments and local businesses, join students in their health and fitness workouts ❏ **School Opening:** I can assist in planning or volunteer to assist in school opening activities ❏ **Reading:** I can read to students in classrooms, tell stories or recite poetry, perform a puppet show, donate books, organize book fairs, contact publishers for book donations, assist the media specialist ❏ **Writing/Publishing:** I can volunteer to assist students in writing and publishing their work ❏ **Cooking:** I can cook snacks for testing week, make treats for the teachers, cook ethnic dishes to support international celebrations, or to support academic or other school-wide celebrations ❏ **Real Estate:** I can help teachers and support staff buy a home in the community ❏ **Gardening:** I can maintain flower beds or design landscaping ❏ **Classrooms:** I can volunteer in the classroom ❏ **Chaperone:** I can chaperone field trips, the school dance, or prom ❏ **Preacher:** I can bless the school and everyone in it ❏ **Nurse or Doctor:** I can spearhead a healthy kid day and ensure that every student gets off to a healthy start to the school year ❏ **Construction Worker:** I can build something or donate building materials ❏ **Automobile Mechanic:** I can keep the teachers' cars running ❏ **Workshop Presenter:** I can provide training for parents, teachers, or students ❏ **Give Money:** I can give money—the possibilities are endless.

Activity 25

Parent Involvement

Objective

Identify gifts, talents, and interest that you can contribute to supporting the efforts of your child's school.

Things that you can contribute to the school:

_____

_____

_____

_____

Other people who will support your efforts:

_____

_____

_____

_____

You are not going to be the only parent who cares about his or her child. Identify other parents who will be willing to work with you and put together your team. A small group of parents who are working together on activities related to their passion or areas of interest can have a tremendous impact on the school and positive influence in the lives of children.

Activity 26

Classroom Involvement

Overview

Ask your child's teacher, his or her grade-level or subject-area team, or your child's coach to complete this form.

Things that parents can do to contribute to your classroom, department, or program:

_____

_____

_____

_____

_____

_____

_____

_____

_____

_____

_____

Activity 27

School-wide Involvement

Overview

Ask your child's principal, assistant principal, or counselor to complete this form.

Things that parents can do to contribute to the school:

_____

_____

_____

_____

_____

_____

_____

_____

_____

_____

_____

_____

_____

A Pledge to Myself

Today, I pledge to be

    the best possible me.

No matter how good I am

I know that I can become better.

Today, I pledge to build

    on the work of yesterday

Which will lead me

    into the rewards of tomorrow.

Today, I pledge to feed

    my mind: knowledge

    my body: strength, and

    my spirit: faith.

Today, I pledge to reach

    new goals

    new challenges, and

    new horizons.

Today, I pledge to listen

    to the beat of my drummer

Who leads me onward

    in search of dreams.

Today, I pledge to believe in me.

       — Mychal Wynn

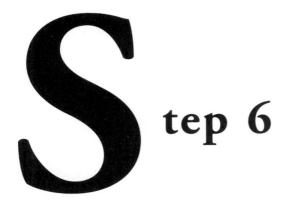

Step 6

Tell Teachers How to Best Communicate With You

It is important to have good communication with your child's teachers. Let teachers know what you expect in terms of behavior, classroom participation, homework, class work, and grades. Ask each teacher for suggestions about the best way for the two of you to keep in touch. It is important for the teacher to know that you want to be involved and that you want the teacher to contact you whenever there is a problem.

Ten Steps to Helping Your Child Succeed in School, p. 122

Step 6 Overview

Step 6 (pp. 122 - 134 in the book) involves establishing effective home-school communication. You and your child's teachers must agree on a primary communication method. If you want your child's teachers to call, tell them when, where, and at what time. If you want them to send notes home, tell them what you need them to do to confirm that your child gives you the note! In some cases, you may have to sign and return the note or write your response in your child's agenda/student planner.

If your child needs a little "push" to ensure that he or she studies for tests and quizzes, tell your child's teacher to send a note home to let you, know well in advance. Ask your child's teacher to send a rubric or study guide so you can ensure your child studies the correct material and so you can pretest your child on the material being covered. Use the "Assignment Log" at the end of this step and the "Teacher Assessment Form," and "Daily Notes Sheet" in the next step to help your child to stay organized and to maintain open lines of communication with his or her teachers.

Activity 28

Home-School Communication

Effective home-school communication begins with identifying the best means of contact between home and school. For example, many parents are accustomed to text messaging while many teachers are only beginning to use e-mail. Some teachers check their e-mails daily, sometimes hourly, whereas grandparents, particularly, have never used e-mail. Gather the following information and answer the questions on the following page for each of your child's teachers. Below is a quick quiz to assess the current level of contact that you have with your child's teachers.

Communication Quiz

Teacher: _____ Subject: _____
Preferred means of communication: E-mail   Phone   Note   Agenda
Level of Contact: ❑ Frequent   ❑ Some   ❑ Little   ❑ None

Teacher: _____ Subject: _____
Preferred means of communication: E-mail   Phone   Note   Agenda
Level of Contact: ❑ Frequent   ❑ Some   ❑ Little   ❑ None

Teacher: _____ Subject: _____
Preferred means of communication: E-mail   Phone   Note   Agenda
Level of Contact: ❑ Frequent   ❑ Some   ❑ Little   ❑ None

Teacher: _____ Subject: _____
Preferred means of communication: E-mail   Phone   Note   Agenda
Level of Contact: ❑ Frequent   ❑ Some   ❑ Little   ❑ None

Teacher: _____ Subject: _____
Preferred means of communication: E-mail   Phone   Note   Agenda
Level of Contact: ❑ Frequent   ❑ Some   ❑ Little   ❑ None

Teacher: _____ Subject: _____
Preferred means of communication: E-mail   Phone   Note   Agenda
Level of Contact: ❑ Frequent   ❑ Some   ❑ Little   ❑ None

Name: _____ Subject: _____

Preferred means of communication: E-mail   Phone   Note   Agenda

E-mail: _____

Web site: _____

Phone: _____

Planning Time: _____ Room # _____

Name: _____ Subject: _____

Preferred means of communication: E-mail   Phone   Note   Agenda

E-mail: _____

Web site: _____

Phone: _____

Planning Time: _____ Room # _____

Name: _____ Subject: _____

Preferred means of communication: E-mail   Phone   Note   Agenda

E-mail: _____

Web site: _____

Phone: _____

Planning Time: _____ Room # _____

Name: _____ Subject: _____

Preferred means of communication: E-mail   Phone   Note   Agenda

E-mail: _____

Web site: _____

Phone: _____

Planning Time: _____ Room # _____

Activity 29

Parent Communication

I am concerned about my child's (_____)
academic achievement. Whenever possible, I would like to provide timely intervention
to ensure that my child submits his or her work as expected, is prepared for tests and
quizzes, takes advantage of extra credit opportunities and is behaving appropriately in
class.

Listed below are my preferred methods of communication:

Name: _____

Preferred means of communication: E-mail   Phone   Note   Agenda

E-mail: _____

Phone: _____ Best time to reach me: _____

Alternate phone: _____ Best time to reach me: _____

Based on my previous experiences, I am checking the areas in which my child has
experienced difficulties in the past:

❏ Submitting assignments on time   ❏ Behavior

❏ Peer pressure   ❏ Test/quiz preparation

❏ Effective note-taking   ❏ Organization

❏ Class participation   ❏ Cutting class

❏ Informing me of project due dates   ❏ Gang activity

❏ Regular routines   ❏ Distraction by girls/boys

❏ Balancing school work and activities   ❏ Lack of initiative

❏ Preparing for tests in different subjects   ❏ Extrinsic motivation

❏ Letting teacher know when he/she is confused   ❏ Struggles in this subject

Date Submitted	Date Returned	Grade	Assignment Log

S tep 7

Prepare for School

S tep back and take a look at your household and assess what must be done to prepare for the school year. If organization is not one of your strengths, ask friends, relatives, or other parents to help you get organized and prepared for the first day of school.

Ten Steps to Helping Your Child Succeed in School, p. 135

Step 7 Overview

Step 7 (pp. 135 - 150 in the book) involves preparing for the school year. Despite the fact that everyone knows when the first day of school occurs, many parents still discover themselves running out of time in preparing for the school year. Following are some of the many things outlined in this chapter of the book:

- *How to get organized for the school year*

- *The importance of getting the supply list well in advance*

- *How to establish boxes, drawers, or permanent locations in your home for papers and supplies*

- *Why you should request a student registration form, school calendar, and immunization schedule from the school prior to the end of the current school year*

- *The importance of completing the school's registration form and gathering any information required to register your child for the forthcoming school year, e.g., immunization records, birth certificate, social security card, proof of address, etc.*

Activity 30

Prepare for the School Year

Step back, take a critical look at your household, and assess what must be done to ensure that you are adequately prepared for the school year:

1. Note the first day of school and early release days.

❑ First day of school: _____   ❑ Early Release Day: _____

❑ Early Release Day: _____   ❑ Early Release Day: _____

❑ Early Release Day: _____   ❑ Early Release Day: _____

❑ Early Release Day: _____   ❑ Early Release Day: _____

2. Ask the school for a supply list or send a note to each of your child's teachers.

"What supplies, resources, or supplemental materials, e.g., dictionary, math workbooks, thesaurus, etc., would you recommend to assist my child to be successful in your classroom?"

3. Establish the following boxes, drawers, or permanent locations in your home:

❑ School box—used to keep all school related papers.

❑ Supply box—used for all school supplies.

❑ Resource box—used for such resources as Dictionary, Atlas, Thesaurus, grammar guide, math/science study guides, etc.

❑ The book, *A High School Plan for Students with College-Bound Dreams*, is a valuable resource for parents of high school students. The book outlines how to prepare boxes for college applications, financial-aid information, and other important papers pertaining to the college admissions process.

❑ The book, *A Middle School Plan for Students with College-Bound Dreams*, is a valuable resource for parents of middle school students. The book outlines how to track middle school achievement and how to maximize the middle school experience.

4. *Request the following information from the school prior to the end of the current school year:*

- ❑ Student registration form ❑ School calendar
- ❑ Immunization schedule

5. *Complete the school's registration form and create a folder containing the following information:*

- ❑ Social Security card ❑ Proof of address
- ❑ Immunization records ❑ Emergency contact information
- ❑ Parents of high school seniors need to gather W2 forms and tax info

6. *Prepare 5 large envelopes*

- ❑ Write your child's name and the name, address, and telephone number of the school onto each envelope.

7. *Place the following information into each envelope (note: some of the information may not be available until after the first day of school):*

- ❑ Your contact information, e.g., work phone, cell phone, pager, work hours, lunch time, etc.
- ❑ A copy of your child's class schedule.
- ❑ The name and contact information of each teacher.
- ❑ The names of the administrators, office staff, and your child's counselor.
- ❑ Locker information, including the location and combination of your child's locker.
- ❑ Bus number, including pick-up and drop-off times.

8. *Place each envelope in the following places:*

- ❑ Your car ❑ Your job
- ❑ Your school box ❑ One to each emergency contact

9. *Review the supply lists, gather the necessary school supplies, and place them into the supply box. Typical supplies would include:*

❑	Three-hole college-ruled paper	❑	Spiral notebooks
❑	Plain unlined white paper	❑	Construction paper
❑	Tape	❑	Glue sticks
❑	Paper clips	❑	Stapler/staples
❑	Erasers	❑	Highlight markers
❑	White out	❑	Three ring folders/binders
❑	Clear report covers	❑	Colored pencils, markers, or crayons
❑	Pencil sharpener	❑	Calculator
❑	Scissors	❑	Three-hole puncher
❑	#2 Pencils and ink pens	❑	Ruler

10. *Gather the needed resource materials and place into the resource box.*

Typical resource materials would include:

❑	Dictionary	❑	Thesaurus
❑	English Grammar Guide	❑	Atlas

11. *Establish a permanent location for backpacks, lunch boxes, and soiled athletic clothes, e.g., P.E. uniform, jerseys, etc.*

_____

12. *Establish your school day routine such as:*

❑	Wake-up time _____	❑	Bedtime _____
❑	Homework time and study location		

❑ Morning and evening routines, e.g., bath, vitamins, reading, laying out clothes, etc.

13. *Post a calendar in your kitchen and write all of the important school dates on to the calendar, e.g., standardized testing, short days, holidays, progress reports, report cards, parent-teacher conferences, PTA/PTSA meetings, spring break, etc.*

Activity 31

Homework Rules

Homework is not as intense during the first few weeks of school as it will be as the semester progresses. Therefore, it is important before the school year begins to have a "Homework Plan." Take what you have learned through the previous activities into account as you develop your homework rules. Develop a plan that is responsive to your child's needs and one that your child will feel capable of following. Some children do best by coming home and doing their homework as soon as they arrive home, while others need to take a break and relax before they get started on their homework. Experiment with different methods to identify the one that works best for your child.

Review the "Homework Rules" on the following page and adjust accordingly, based on the needs of your child and the dynamics of your household, e.g., when you get home from work, if your child has older siblings to work with him or her, if your child participates in after-school programs, or extracurricular activities.

Whatever you decide upon for your homework rules (see sample on next page), be sure that you do not allow your child an opportunity to do the things that are important to him (e.g., talking on the telephone, television, video games, sports, etc.) until he has completed his homework and whatever else is important to you.

Create a work environment consistent with what you outlined earlier as your child's learning style. While background music is good for one child, it may be distracting for another. If you allow your child to listen to background music while he does his homework, try to make sure that it is music only, no vocals. No matter what your child says, the lyrics are likely to interrupt his concentration. He is more likely to remember the lyrics to the song rather than the words or facts in the book he is reading.

Ten Steps to Helping Your Child Succeed in School: Workbook © Mychal Wynn

Homework Rules

1. Begin all homework within 30 minutes of getting home from school.

2. Place all homework into a stack on the kitchen table when completed.

3. Ensure that homework is reviewed and error free before you leave the table.

4. You earn 10 minutes of television time for each error-free assignment (maximum television on school nights is 30 minutes).

5. Read for 30 minutes after homework is completed.

6. You may not have company or receive telephone calls until after homework and reading have been completed.

7. Clean up your area and put away your books and supplies after completing your homework.

Note:

These rules are subject to change based on grades, performance, level of responsibility, attitude, behavior, and number of missed assignments.

Activity 32

Different Routines for Different Learning Styles

Try to develop your routines prior to the beginning of the school year. Analytical children typically want organization and order. They like step-by-step instructions. While Global children also need routines, their routines will be easier to follow if the family sits down and develops the routines together. Consider the following when developing your before- and after-school routines. Compare your routines against the sample on the following page.

1. What time will your child need to wake up to ensure that he or she is ready for the school bus or to be driven to school?

2. How much time should be allowed for your child to get cleaned up, dressed, and to eat breakfast?

3. What do you want your child to do in the mornings, e.g., shower, brush teeth, comb hair, floss?

4. What will your child need to do to ensure that he or she has his or her homework, important papers, or notes from you to his or her teacher?

5. Where will your child do his or her homework?

6. What are your child's daily chores?

7. Where should your child place his or her backpack and lunch box?

8. How much TV time will you allow your child to watch during the week?

9. Should your child eat an after-school snack?

After reviewing the "Sample Daily Routines" on the following page, use the forms to create before- and after-school routines that are appropriate for your child, your household circumstances, your child's learning style, and your child's level of maturity. Make copies of the "Daily Notes Sheet" and "Teacher Assessment Form" for each class. Begin the school year by reviewing your child's notes daily, and communicate with his or her classroom teachers regularly, to ensure that his or her performance is meeting both your and his or her teacher's expectations.

Sample Daily Routines

Morning Routine

	Time	Description	M	T	W	T	F
❑	6:00	Wake up, make up bed, feed cat, clean kitty litter	❑	❑	❑	❑	❑
❑	6:15	Eat breakfast	❑	❑	❑	❑	❑
❑	6:30	Brush teeth, wash up, get dressed	❑	❑	❑	❑	❑
❑	6:50	Review planner, get lunch box and back pack	❑	❑	❑	❑	❑
❑	7:00	Go to bus stop	❑	❑	❑	❑	❑

Afternoon Routine

	Time	Description					
❑	3:00	Place binders, planner, and books into back pack	❑	❑	❑	❑	❑
❑	3:05	Take bus home	❑	❑	❑	❑	❑
❑	3:30	Take out lunch box and review planner	❑	❑	❑	❑	❑
❑	3:45	Homework (if no homework, read!)	❑	❑	❑	❑	❑
❑	4:45	High-energy snack	❑	❑	❑	❑	❑
❑	5:15	Prepare water and dress for football practice	❑	❑	❑	❑	❑
❑	5:45	Leave for football practice					

Evening Routine

	Time	Description					
			❑	❑	❑	❑	❑
❑	8:45	Return from football practice and shower	❑	❑	❑	❑	❑
❑	9:00	Eat dinner	❑	❑	❑	❑	❑
❑	9:20	Brush teeth and prepare for bed	❑	❑	❑	❑	❑
❑	9:30	Go to bed	❑	❑	❑	❑	❑

Time	Daily Before School Schedule

Time	Daily After School Schedule

Class	Daily Classroom Routine

SUBJECT:

TODAY'S DATE: _____ **MIDTERM:** _____ **FINAL:** _____

TEST/PROJECT: _____

_____

_____

DAILY WORK: _____

_____

_____

HOMEWORK: _____

_____

_____

NOTES FROM WHAT WAS COVERED TODAY: _____

_____

_____

_____

_____

_____

_____

_____

Daily Notes Sheet

PARENT INITIAL

SUBJECT:

TODAY'S DATE: _____ **STUDENT:** _____ **GR____**

BRINGS APPROPRIATE MATERIALS TO CLASS

❑ *OUTSTANDING*   ❑ *SATISFACTORY*   ❑ *NEEDS IMPROVEMENT*

COMMENTS:

_____

_____

_____

CLASSROOM PARTICIPATION

❑ *OUTSTANDING*   ❑ *SATISFACTORY*   ❑ *NEEDS IMPROVEMENT*

COMMENTS:

_____

_____

_____

COMPLETES AND TURNS IN CLASS WORK

❑ *OUTSTANDING*   ❑ *SATISFACTORY*   ❑ *NEEDS IMPROVEMENT*

COMMENTS:

_____

_____

_____

BEHAVIOR

❑ *OUTSTANDING*   ❑ *SATISFACTORY*   ❑ *NEEDS IMPROVEMENT*

COMMENTS:

_____

_____

RECOMMENDATIONS FOR IMPROVEMENT

_____

_____

_____

_____

_____

Teacher Assessment Form

TEACHER INITIAL

Step 8

Prepare for Testing

Despite the fact that schools throughout the country are being measured by how well students perform on standardized tests, parents typically receive very little information advising them of what they can do to help their child perform well on such tests. Not only will higher test scores help your child's school meet your State Accountability Standards they will provide your child with opportunities to do more interesting and engaging work. Schools that are performing well devote more time to engaging students in projects, performances, extracurricular activities, field trips, and more academically-related opportunities.

Ten Steps to Helping Your Child Succeed in School, p. 153

Step 8 Overview

Step 8 (pp. 151 - 162 in the book) provides strategies for preparing your child for testing. Your child's performance on classroom and standardized tests will impact his or her class placement, course offerings, and opportunities to participant in summer camps and enrichment programs. While good grades can provide your child with a broad range of academic awards and recognition, high test scores can provide your child with a wide range of opportunities from elementary through high school and scholarship money for college. Ultimately, grades and standardized test scores will determine the scope of your child's college choices.

Your child's success in school will also have an impact on the range of programs, camps, activities, and clubs in which he or she may have the opportunity to participate. In many school districts, high test scores will qualify your child for the Talented and Gifted Program; academically-gifted classes; high school honors and AP classes; state, local, and national competitions; and academic-oriented clubs, e.g., National Honor Society, Beta Club, etc.

Activity 33

Prepare for Class Testing

Objective

Establish routines that will assist in preparing your child to perform well on classroom testing.

Overview

Performing well on tests, as is a child's performance in athletic competitions, requires practice, coaching, focus, and preparation. Anything you can do to support, encourage, and prepare your child do well is in the best interest of your child.

The following steps will assist in helping your child do better on tests within the classroom:

❑ Contact each of your child's teachers and ask for the best way for you to be informed of announced tests and quizzes.

❑ Ask each teacher if he or she provides grading rubrics or study guides and ensure that you child is organized so that grading rubrics and study guides do not get misplaced.

❑ Develop a routine for helping your child to review the material and test your child at home several times before tests are given in class.

❑ Experiment with the different approaches and study locations to identify the way in which your child most easily processes and recalls information.

1. Allow your child to study the material in whatever way he of she feels most comfortable. Observe how he or she studies. Then test your child on the material that he or she has studied and determine if his or her study method was effective.

2. Have your child study in a quiet location for a predetermined period of time (e.g., 15 minutes) and then test him or her on the material that was covered. Was the study approach effective?

3. Have your child study in a location that has background noise (talking, radio, television, etc.) for a predetermined period of time (e.g., 15 minutes) and then test him or her on the material that was covered. Was the study approach effective?

4. Have your child read what he or she is studying aloud for a predetermined period of time (e.g., 15 minutes) and then test him or her on the material that was covered. Was the study approach effective?

5. Have your child read the material aloud AND take notes for a predetermined period of time (e.g., 15 minutes) and then test him or her on the material that was covered. Was the study approach effective?

6. Have your child read the material AND walk around for a predetermined period of time (e.g., 15 minutes) and then test him or her on the material that was covered. Was the study approach effective?

Check the approach that appeared most effective

❑ Quiet   ❑ Background noise

❑ Reading aloud   ❑ Reading aloud and taking notes

❑ Reading quietly and taking notes   ❑ Reading aloud and walking around

❑ Sitting at a desk or table   ❑ Laying on the bed or floor

The night before the test, make sure that your child gets a good night's sleep and has a healthy breakfast on the morning of the test.

Activity 34

Prepare for State/National Testing

Objective

Establish routines that will assist in preparing your child to perform well on state and national testing.

Overview

Performance on state and national testing can have far-reaching implications for your child. Some tests will determine course placement for the following school year, other tests will determine if your child is able to pass to the next grade, while other tests will determine if your child receives his or her high school diploma.

Standardized test dates vary by school district and by grade level. Some school districts give children different types of tests. In Georgia, students take the Iowa Test of Basic Skills (ITBS), Criterion Reference Competency Tests (CRCT), and high school exit exams. In Florida, students take the Florida Comprehensive Achievement Tests (FCAT), and the Comprehensive Test of Basic Skills (CTBS). In California, students take the California Standards Tests (CSTs) and California High School Exit Exam (CHSEE), In Maryland, students take the Maryland School Assessment (MSA). In Texas, students take the Texas Assessment of Knowledge and Skills (TAKS). Many states require that students pass high school exit exams prior to receiving their high school diplomas.

The following steps will assist in helping your child to perform better on tests within the classroom:

❑   Ask your child's teacher or counselor if the class will be doing practice tests

❑   Go to your State Department of Education web site to identify study guides, practice tests, and supplemental study materials

❑   If your child demonstrates an interest and is capable of studying beyond his or her grade level, identify the necessary supplemental materials for the next grade level

The following steps will help your child prepare for standardized testing:

- ❑ Test/date: _____
- ❑ Test/date: _____
- ❑ Test/date: _____
- ❑ Test/date: _____
- ❑ Test/date: _____
- ❑ Test/date: _____
- ❑ Test/date: _____
- ❑ Test/date: _____

- ❑ Practice tests, study guides, or supplemental materials for each test.

- ❑ Encourage your child each day during the week of testing as he or she leaves home and praise your child's effort each day as he or she returns home.

- ❑ Encourage your child to read and use test language, e.g., compare, contrast, mean, median, sum, etc.

- ❑ Prepare in advance your child's clothes for each day of the week of testing.

- ❑ Ensure that your child gets plenty of rest each night before testing.

- ❑ Ensure that your child has a healthy breakfast each morning.

- ❑ Ensure that your household is as quiet and as peaceful as possible during the week of testing.

- ❑ Keep after-school activities to a minimum during the week of testing.

- ❑ Review and practice material each night prior to the next day of testing.

- ❑ Encourage and help your child to relax each morning of testing. Do not pressure him or her to do well; instead, just encourage him or her to do his or her best.

- ❑ Reinforce the test-taking strategies each morning with your son or daughter.

- ❑ Have a celebration at the end of testing. Have a pizza party, go to a movie, or go to the park. Let your child know you are pleased with his or her effort.

- ❑ Use a binder or box to immediately file your child's test scores when you receive them, which may be several months after testing.

Step 9

Talk About What Your Child Is Learning

Step 9 Overview

Step 9 (pp. 163 - 168 in the book) provides commonsense strategies to ensure that parents are in touch with what their child is learning, or isn't learning throughout the school year. Parents must demonstrate an interest in what their children are working on in school. Get into the habit of saying to your child each day after school, "Tell me what happened in school today." Show enthusiasm about the things your child is excited about and try to find ways of getting your child to be excited about things that have to be learned, but may not be as interesting.

Our older son studied archeology in third grade. We took copies of his archeology facts with us during spring break and talked about archeology in the car during our drive from Atlanta, Georgia, to Washington, D.C. When studying state capitals in fourth grade, we quizzed him each day at the grocery store, in the barbershop, and at the mall. He liked it so much that he began asking adults if they knew certain state capitals. "Mr. Ralston, I'll bet you don't know the state capital of Maine. Ms. Kimberly, I'll bet you don't know the state capital of Alaska."

Activity 35

What Happened Today at School?

Objective

Establish a household culture that reinforces the importance of education.

Overview

Your child has arrived home. He or she is tired, does not want to talk, but you want to know how his or her day was. As the parent you have to ask questions and communicate with your child about his or her day. Starting this at an early age builds a bridge of communication. Now do not get me wrong: there will be times when your child will not want to talk, but talking with him or her at an early age helps to lay a foundation for the years ahead.

Questions to ask:

1. What did you learn today?

2. What fun things did you do today?

3. Did you meet anyone new?

4. Did anything funny happen?

5. Tell me about your day.

6. What did you eat for lunch?

7. What was the most interesting thing that you learned or did?

When your child is younger, he or she may not be able to verbally communicate the events of his or her day in great detail. This would be a great opportunity to stimulate his or her artistic side. Have him or her draw a picture about what he or she learned during the day or ate during lunch. This kind of activity is a great opportunity to develop a home journal.

What Did You Learn in School Today?

What are the classes and activities that your child most enjoys? Ask questions about these activities each day and look for opportunities for your child to share the joy that he or she feels when studying or participating in these activities:

_____

_____

_____

_____

_____

_____

_____

What are the classes and activities that your child least enjoys or struggles the most with? Ask questions about these activities each day and look for opportunities to encourage your child's efforts:

_____

_____

_____

_____

_____

_____

_____

Step 10

Stay Focused on the Dream

Step 10 Overview

Step 10 (pp. 169 - 180 in the book) will assist you in your efforts to unlock your child's dreams and aspirations. Some children readily affirm their dreams, while others rarely share their hopes and aspirations. There is not a one-size-fits-all education that every child needs. Each child needs to have an education that will enable him or her to pursue his or her dreams and aspirations. Despite all the things that they are taught in the classroom—all of the homework they are given, all of the field trips, all of the research papers, all of the tests, and all of the other stuff they are suppose to remember and are required to know—most children will go to school from kindergarten through the twelfth grade and never have an assignment, homework, or research paper designed to help them discover their *dreams* and *aspirations*.

When you were in school, how many teachers—from kindergarten through the twelfth grade—spent any time talking about your dreams? How many guest speakers were invited into your school or classroom who had lived your dreams and who were invited to talk to you about what you must do to achieve *your* dreams?

Activity 36

What Are Your Child's Dreams?

Objective

Ensure that you develop an educational plan that will best assist your child in pursuing his or her dreams and aspirations.

Overview

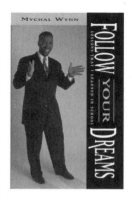

When we talk about dreams, we too frequently think of jobs. Yes, there are in fact "dream jobs," but jobs are often vehicles that carry us to other dreams, e.g., pursuing a social cause, paying for our child's education, taking a cruise, feeding the hungry, reducing crime, publishing a book, starting a business, buying a home, buying a new car, etc. Help your child to develop short-term dreams and long-term dreams, each leading to short-term goals and long-term goals. The book, *Follow Your Dreams: Lessons That I Learned in School,* and *My Dreams: Student Journal,* are excellent resources to initiate the discussion about dreams and importance of education.

Consider the following:

1. What types of things does your child enjoy doing?

    For example, does he or she like playing video games, going to the movies, going to a theme park, riding a bicycle, going to a baseball game, drawing, talking, singing, playing an instrument, acting, dressing up, cooking, shopping, etc.? Use his or her interests to inspire dreams of doing, of seeing, of overcoming, of learning, or of changing.

    _____

    _____

    _____

2. What talents, special abilities, or intelligences does your child have that could lead to a career aspiration or educational goal?

The child who talks a lot could dream of becoming a motivational speaker or television personality. The child who likes to draw could dream of becoming a cartoonist or computer animator. The child who enjoys cooking could dream of becoming a chef or of owning a restaurant. The possibilities are endless!

_____

_____

_____

_____

_____

_____

_____

_____

3. What subjects in school does your child enjoy most?

The child who loves history could dream of becoming a historian. The child who loves math could dream of becoming an astronaut or mathematician. The child who loves English or literature could dream of becoming a writer, publisher, playwright, or English teacher. The child who loves science could dream of becoming a doctor or research scientist. The child who loves sports could dream of becoming an athlete, sports commentator, orthopedic surgeon, personal fitness trainer, coach, or health club owner.

_____

_____

_____

_____

4. What programs or activities does your child find most challenging or most enjoyable?

_____

_____

_____

_____

_____

_____

5. Look at each area of your child's seemingly negative behaviors (talking too much, tapping on his or her desk, clowning around in class) and think of positive uses to inspire long-term dreams and aspirations.

_____

_____

_____

_____

_____

_____

_____

_____

_____

_____

Activity 37

Ways To Expand Your Child's Dreams

Objective

Nurture your child's dreams and aspirations by increasing access to reading materials and enrichment programs.

Overview

When many people think of a dream, they imagine something far-fetched or something intangible; that is what makes something a dream, right? Well, let's change our children's thinking of a dream from something far-fetched to something you plan for. Let's teach our children that a dream is something a person thinks about, talks to people about, sets goals for achieving, and learns to pursue with passion. It is not necessarily a job or living somewhere exotic, but a state of mind. Children should set both short- and long-term goals that are consistent with pursuing their educational, career, and life dreams.

Dream Envelopes

One of the most important things at the beginning of the year is helping teachers to get to know your child—his or her learning styles, intelligences, personalities, strengths, weaknesses, and yes, his or her dreams. As children enter elementary school, they have many dreams and are motivated to think about them and share them with classmates. You must identify and nurture those dreams and aspirations during the primary grades. Talk to teachers, counselors, and other parents about enrichment programs, summer camps, after-school programs, and local opportunities to pave the way into richly rewarding and passionate pursuits through your child's middle and high school years.

Get a poster board and fold it in half. Staple along the sides. Your child can collect magazines and decorate the outside of the envelope with pictures, words, and images that relate to his or her dreams. Place school work, magazines, business cards, and information gathered during the school year that relates to his or her dreams inside of the envelope.

Ten Steps to Helping Your Child Succeed in School: Workbook © Mychal Wynn

Epilogue

Things to do at the End of the School Year

Epilogue Overview

After surviving another school year, it is time for a celebration. Spend time with your child at the park, walking on the beach, taking in a movie or going anywhere you and your child feel comfortable and happy. Take time to exhale and to reflect on the successes of you and your child throughout the school year. Rarely does a child qualify for the honor roll without his or her parents putting in a lot of time helping him or her to stay on top of his or her academic tasks. Rarely does a top athlete achieve success without a parent paying registration fees, buying equipment, and taking him or her to practices and tournaments. Rarely does a student win a Spelling Bee or Science Fair without a parent's willingness to turn his or her home into a training camp or laboratory. Celebrate! You deserve to!

Activity 38

Year-end Parent Assessment

Objective

Reflect on the challenges and successes of the school year in preparation for developing your action plan for the coming school year.

Overview

As you reflect on the school year, answer the following question for yourself and your child:

How did you feel about each of your teachers?

- Take a sheet of paper and write one paragraph describing each teacher.

- Write down five adjectives that best describe each teacher: e.g., caring, positive, boring, engaging, enlightening, fun, nasty, loving, kind, inspiring, encouraging, etc.

Activity 39

Year-end Student Assessment

Overview

Complete this activity for each teacher and extracurricular activity involvement.

1. How did you feel about the teacher or coach?

   _____

   _____

   _____

2. Write down five adjectives which best describe this teacher or coach: e.g., caring, positive, boring, engaging, enlightening, fun, nasty, loving, kind, inspiring, encouraging, etc.

   _____

   _____

   _____

   _____

3. What was the most interesting thing you learned in this class or activity?

   _____

   _____

   _____

4. What did you enjoy most in this class or activity?

   _____

   _____

   _____

5. What were the worst things you experienced in this class or activity?

_____

_____

_____

6. Was this one of your best subjects or activities?   Y or N

7. How would you describe this subject or activity? Difficult Challenging Easy

8. What kind of activity would you liked to have done more often?

_____

_____

_____

9. What would you liked to have done less?

_____

_____

_____

10. What did you learn or experience this year that will best prepare you to be successful in this class or activity next year?

_____

_____

_____

11. Is there anything you would like to do or learn over the summer to better prepare for this class or activity next school year?

_____

_____

_____

Activity 40

Year-end Teacher Letters

Objective

Sharing you and your child's thoughts with your child's teachers.

Overview

Use the answers to the questions in the previous activity to assist your child in writing a letter to each teacher sharing his or her honest thoughts regarding the school year (e.g., likes and dislikes, best and worst learning experiences, and high and low points of the school year, etc.). Through this process, I have found that my children have oftentimes had very different impressions of the school and its teachers than I did.

I have discovered, on more than one occasion, that my son loved teachers whom I did not particularly like. It is these teachers for whom I have found the letters most valuable. Rather than leaving them with the negative impression they often received from me through my many notes (and possibly my attitude during parent-teacher conferences), they are left with a positive letter from a child who liked them and enjoyed being in their classes. Keep a copy of the letters in your school box and send a copy of the letters to the principal.

The answers to your questions, together with your child's letters, provide a glimpse into your child's feelings about the school year. It is important for you as a parent to take the time to "talk to" and "listen to" your child. Let your child know that someone cares about what he or she thought about the teachers, the subjects studied, the field trips taken, and the many things that happened in your child's life during the school year. It is important to know the best and worst things that stand out in your child's mind after the school year is over. This knowledge will help you to begin planning for the next school year.

Ten Steps to Helping Your Child Succeed in School: Workbook © Mychal Wynn

Sample Year-end Letter

Dear Ms. Appleyard:

I would like to thank you for a great school year. You turned our class into a family and taught us how to get along with each other, to be respectful, and to support each other. This was my best school year ever. I am sorry to see fifth grade come to an end, but I guess that it is time for me to move on to middle school and beyond. I will never forget how you taught us to look for and appreciate our gifts. As you taught us, "Y B Normal?" I no longer feel embarrassed about being different or that I have to talk like or behave like anyone else... "Y B Normal?"

You were my best teacher ever and I will never forget you.

Sincerely,

Jalani Wynn
Rising Sixth Grader

P. S. To ensure that you do not forget me, I will come back often to visit your classroom:)

Activity 41

Year-end Organization

Objective

Before rushing off to vacations, take the time to celebrate the ending of one school year and begin pre-planning for the coming school year.

Overview

Gather all of the your child's work, awards, and special memories from the school year and compile them into a collage, poster, or scrapbook. Share this collection with your child's teacher at the beginning of the next school year.

Store the rest of your child's school-year materials. This year has represented another step toward your child's pursuing his or her dreams and aspirations. Make note of the people (e.g., teachers, coaches, principals, preachers, friends, family, school staff, tutors, etc.), who have played a role in the growth, development, maturation, and nurturing of your child. Take time to update them on your child's progress over the ensuing years as a means of continually thanking them for their role in your child's development and in making them a permanent part of your child's ongoing success.

Our older son is about to graduate from high school and we are sending a newsletter to each of the people, whom over the years have played a role in his growth and development. Through the newsletter, we are recognizing their role in the village, i.e., "It takes a village to raise a child." We are sharing his high school accomplishments and some facts about the college he will be enrolling in. Each person, in his or her own way has contributed to his high school success and his forthcoming admission into college.

Finally, keep in mind that the world is changing with each new day. What was considered impossible yesterday is possible today. What was thought unbelievable yesterday is not only believable, but commonplace today. Do not measure your child's potential in terms of what he or she has or has not done. Instead, encourage your child to dream great dreams and to aspire to do great things. Never forget, "Your child is a continuing work-in-progress, a lump of coal that you must untiringly polish into a diamond to reveal his or her divine brilliance."

Ten Steps to Helping Your Child Succeed in School: Workbook © Mychal Wynn

Parental Reflection

While everything is fresh in your mind, take a moment and reflect on the highs and lows of the school year. Make note of those things that you want to repeat during the next school year as well as the lessons that were learned in regard to challenges that you would like to avoid.

_____

_____

_____

_____

_____

_____

_____

_____

_____

_____

_____

_____

_____

_____

_____

_____

_____

Important Resources

Successfully navigating a child's way through a school system from elementary school, through middle school, and through high school is a difficult task—as evidenced by high school graduation rates under 50 percent in many school districts. As parents of two African-American males, my wife and I are keenly aware that the high school graduation rate for students like them is the lowest among all students, with some school districts having an African-American male high school graduation rate well below 50 percent. If this workbook has inspired you to become more involved in ensuring that your child does not become a statistic, then the following resources should assist in your efforts.

A High School Plan for Students with College-Bound Dreams [Wynn]
Book: Item #6903 • [ISBN 1-880463-66-0] • $19.95
Workbook: Item #6905 • [ISBN 1-880463-80-6] • $15.95
Quick Guide: Item #6902 • [ISBN 1-880463-68-7] • $5.95
Binder: Item #6905 • $24.95

Easy-to-follow planning guide for high school students. Helps students to understand how grades, standardized tests, behavior, activities, classes, community service, essays, and the billions of dollars in available scholarship money can all be factored into a plan (beginning in the sixth grade!) that can pave the way into the college(s) of their choice. Provides worksheets for tracking grades, test scores, awards, and class schedules.

A Middle School Plan for Students with College-Bound Dreams [Wynn]
Book • Item #6901 • [ISBN 1-880463-67-9] • $15.95
Workbook: Item #6906 • [ISBN 1-880463-00-8] • $15.95
Quick Guide: Item #6901 • [ISBN 1-880463-05-9] • $5.95

Easy-to-follow planning guide for middle school students. Outlines how to maximize the middle school experience and how to prepare students for high school success as a stepping stone to students' college-bound dreams. Provides worksheets for tracking grades, test scores, awards, and class schedules.

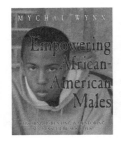

Empowering African-American Males: A Guide to Increasing Black Male Achievement [Wynn]
Book • Item #5101 • [ISBN 1-880463-69-5] • $24.95
Workbook • Item #5102 • [ISBN 1-880463-71-7] • $15.95
Quick Guide • Item #5103 [ISBN 1-880463-03-2] • $5.95

Black males are the most "at-risk" students in America's schools. They are the most likely to be placed into special education, drop out of school, be suspended, be the victims or perpetrators of violent crimes, or be incarcerated. This book outlines a clear, cohesive set of strategies for turning the tide of underachievement into personal empowerment. Provides national discipline and achievement statistics.

The Eagles who Thought They were Chickens [Wynn]
Book • Item #5601 • [ISBN 1-880463-12-1] • $4.95
Teacher's Guide • Item #5602 • [ISBN 1-880463-18-0] • $9.95
Student Activity Book • Item #5603 [ISBN 1-880463-19-9] • $5.95

Chronicles the journey of a great eagle, historically perched at the right hand of the great king in her native Africa, but who is captured and taken aboard a slave ship; the eggs eventually hatched, and the eaglets struggle in the chicken yard, where they are scorned and ridiculed for their differences. The story offers parallels to behaviors in classrooms and on school playgrounds where children are teased by schoolyard "chickens" and bullied by schoolyard "roosters."

Ten Steps to Helping Your Child Succeed in School: Workbook © Mychal Wynn

Share Your Thoughts

Most parents would agree that raising children is a difficult task. Strategies that are effective with one child are ineffective with another. Means of communication that work with one teacher do not with another. In our attempt to publish materials that are parent-friendly, we want to hear your stories.

1. Which activities in this book proved most helpful for you?

2. In what ways did you alter the activities to suit your particular situation?

3. What additional activities or strategies did you use?

4. How open were the teachers and administrators at your child's school to the types of ideas and strategies outlined in this workbook, or in the book, *Ten Steps to Helping Your Child Succeed in School?*

5. What activities or strategies would you like to see in future editions?

Please share your thoughts, ideas, and strategies by postal mail or e-mail:

Rising Sun Publishing
Parenting Workbook Ideas
P.O. Box 70906
Marietta, GA 30007-0906

E-mail: **info@rspublishing.com**
FAX: (770) 587-0862
Subject Line: Parenting Workbook Ideas

To order additional copies or to find the latest edition, go to our web site:

www.rspublishing.com

References

Advanced Placement Report to the Nation (p. 84). (2007). New York, NY: The College Board.

Carey, K. (2005). *One Step from the Finish Line: Higher College Graduation Rates are Within Our Reach*. Washington, DC: Education Trust.

Common Core of Data Public School Data 2004-05. (2007). National Center for Education Statistics. Washington, DC: U.S. Department of Education.

Dunn, R., & Dunn, K. (1992). *Teaching Elementary Students Through Their Individual Learning Styles*. Boston, MA: Allyn & Bacon.

Dunn, R., & Dunn, K. (1993). *Teaching Secondary Students Through Their Individual Learning Styles: Practical Approaches for Grades 7-12*. Boston, MA: Allyn & Bacon.

Dunn, R., Dunn, K. & Perrin, J. (1994). *Teaching Young Children Through Their Individual Learning Styles*. Boston, MA: Allyn & Bacon.

Dunn, R., & Dunn, K. (1999). *The Complete Guide to the Learning Styles Inservice System*. Boston, MA: Allyn & Bacon.

Gardner, Howard. (1983). *Frames of Mind: The Theory of Multiple Intelligences*. New York, NY: Harper & Row.

Greene, J., Winters, M. (2005). *Public High School Graduation and College-Readiness Rates: 1991-2002*. New York, NY: The Manhattan Institute.

Lazear, David. (1991). *Seven Ways of Knowing: Teaching for Multiple Intelligences*. Palatine, IL: IRI/Skylight Publishing.

Myers, Isabel Briggs & Myers, Peter. (1990). *Gifts Differing: Understanding Personality Type*. Palo Alto, CA: CPP Books.

The Condition of Education, 1994: The Educational Progress of Black Students. (1995). National Center for Education Statistics. Washington, DC: U.S. Department of Education.

The Condition of Education, 2001. (2001). National Center for Education Statistics. Washington, DC: U.S. Department of Education.

The Condition of Education, 2006. (2006). National Center for Education Statistics. Washington, DC: U.S. Department of Education.

The Nation's Report Card: America's High School graduates, Results from the 2005 NAEP High School Transcript Study. (2007). National Center for Education Statistics. Washington, DC: U.S. Department of Education.